● McDougal Littell

NEW EDITION

MathThematics

Teacher's Resource Book

 5 Recreation

 6 Flights of Fancy

BOOK **2**

McDougal Littell
A DIVISION OF HOUGHTON MIFFLIN COMPANY

Evanston, Illinois • Boston • Dallas

Acknowledgments

Writers

The authors of *Math Thematics, Books 1–3*, wish to thank the following writers for their contributions to the *Teacher's Resource Books* for the *Math Thematics* program: **Lyle Anderson, Mary Buck, Roslyn Denny, Jean Howard, Deb Johnson, Sallie Morse, Patrick Runkel, Thomas Sanders-Garrett, Bonnie Spence, Christine Tuckerman.**

Image Credits

Photography
Front Cover © Cedar Point, Sandusky, Ohio.

Illustration
All art by McDougal Littell/Houghton Mifflin Co.

THE STEM PROJECT *McDougal Littell Math Thematics®* is based on the field-test versions of The STEM Project curriculum. The STEM Project was supported in part by the

 NATIONAL SCIENCE FOUNDATION

under Grant No. ESI-0137682. Opinions expressed in *McDougal Littell Math Thematics®* are those of the authors and not necessarily those of the National Science Foundation.

ISBN-13: 978-0-547-00114-2
ISBN-10: 0-547-00114-2

12345678 9–BHV–11 10 09 08 07

Contents

About the Teacher's Resource Book

In conjunction with the *Math Thematics*, Book 2, Teacher's Edition, this Resource Book contains all of the teaching support that you need to teach Modules 5 and 6.

Blackline Masters

The teaching support in the Resource Books is organized by module and section and includes the following materials:

Warm-Up Exercises Each Warm-Up page is printed in large easy-to-read type and can be used to create an overhead visual or used as a hand-out. Answers for the exercises are provided at the bottom of the page.

Labsheets Blackline masters used in conjunction with various Exploration questions to present data and extend the scope of the Exploration. Answers are provided in the Teacher's Edition.

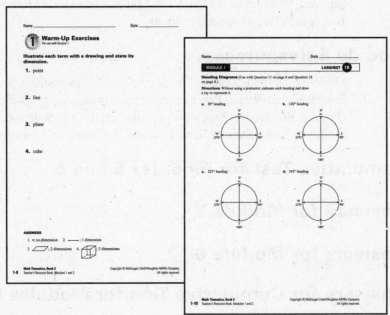

Practice and Applications One to two pages of additional practice for each section in a module, as well as combined practice that covers the whole module.

Study Guide Two to three pages of Study Guide for each section of the module. These Study Guide pages feature key concepts, worked-out examples, and exercises. They can be used for review and reteaching.

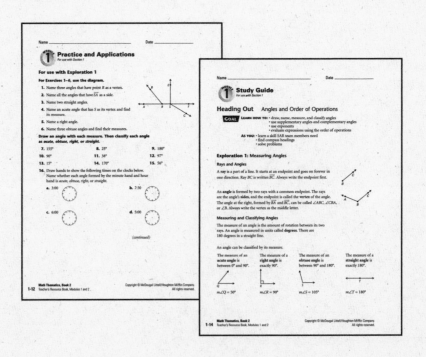

Math Thematics, Book 2
Teacher's Resource Book, Modules 5 and 6

Extended Exploration (E²) Solution Guide

A comprehensive discussion of the Extended Exploration in the student textbook, including how to assess student responses and performance.

Alternate Extended Exploration (Alternate E²) Included in the Teacher's Resource Books for Modules 2, 4, 6, and 7, these extended explorations can be substituted for ones in the student textbook. Materials include teaching notes and assessment procedures.

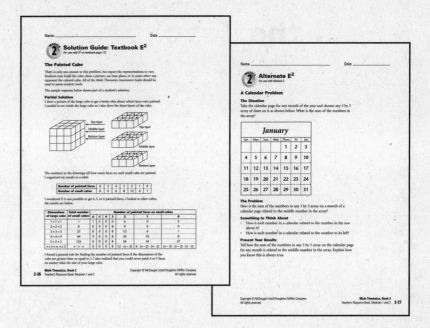

Assessment Assessment options include a diagnostic module pre-test, quick quizzes for each section, a mid-module quiz, and two module tests, Forms A and B.

Cumulative Test A cumulative test on both the modules of this Resource Book.

Module Standardized Test A page of standardized multiple-choice questions for each module.

Module Performance Assessment A Performance Assessment Task for each module.

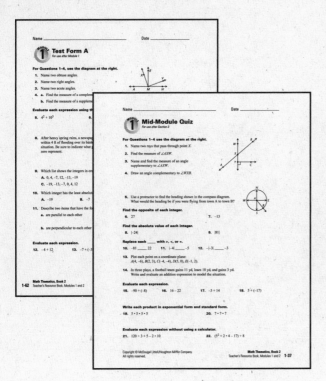

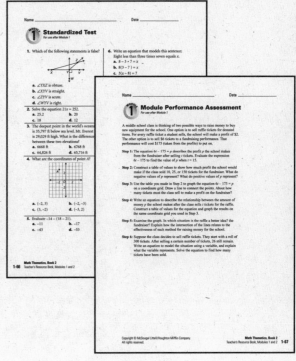

Answers Complete answers to Practice and Applications, Study Guide, Quick Quizzes, and all Assessments for both modules are provided at the back of this Resource Book.

Contents

Book 2	Teacher's Resources for Module 5

Recreation

MODULE 5 Module Diagnostic Test
For use before Module 5

1. 13 cans cost $9.75. Write the unit rate.   (Sec. 1)

2. Write a proportion that could be used to solve the problem below.   (Sec. 1)
You DO NOT need to solve the problem.

If 15 out of 40 people surveyed like spinach, how many people out of 2000
might you expect to like spinach?

3. Contributions of $20, $50, $20, $100, $25, $40, $45, and $80 were given to a charity.   (Sec. 1)
The next person who planned to contribute wanted to give an amount similar to the
other contributions, so he asked, "What is an acceptable amount to give?"

   a. Make a stem-and-leaf plot of the contributions.

   b. Find the following:
   mean = _____   median = _____   mode = _____   range = _____

   c. Give an answer to the contributor's question. Use your stem-and-leaf plot and
   results above to justify your answer.

4. Write two survey questions that you could use to collect data about   (Sec. 2)
the community's interest in obtaining a new swimming facility.

5. Which type of graph(s): stem-and-leaf, histogram,   (Secs. 2 and 3)
scatter plot, or box-and-whisker plot could be made
from the information given in the table?

Number of Hours Spent Sleeping	
Hours	**Frequency**
0–2	2
3–5	5
6–8	14
9–11	6

Module Diagnostic Test
For use before Module 5

6. a. Use graph paper to make a scatter plot of the data in the table below. (Sec. 3)

x	18	8	15	14	10	7	14	6	14	9	17	13	15
y	20	16	18	18	16	15	17	15	16	15	18	16	17

b. Draw a fitted line. Use your line to estimate the value of y when x is 12.

7. Show how to use cross products to solve the proportion. (Sec. 3)

$$\frac{x}{14} = \frac{1.5}{2}$$

8. Use the box-and-whisker plot at the right. (Sec. 3)

Hours Volunteered Last Week

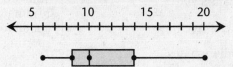

a. Find the median number of hours volunteered.

b. About what percent of the volunteers worked more than 14 hours?

9. Avery Grocery Store gives a discount to 12 of every 130 customers. Approximately what percent of the shoppers receive a discount? (Sec. 4)

A. 10% **B.** 20% **C.** 30% **D.** 40%

10. Find each unknown number. (Sec. 4)

a. 12 is 40% of what number?   **b.** What is 80% of 16?

11. Write the ratio $\frac{15}{17}$ as a percent. Round your answer to the nearest tenth. (Sec. 5)

12. 33% is closest to which of the following "nice" fractions? (Sec. 5)

A. $\frac{2}{5}$ **B.** $\frac{3}{4}$ **C.** $\frac{1}{2}$ **D.** $\frac{1}{3}$

13. Solve to find the percent. 75 is what percent of 30? (Sec. 5)

The Math Gazette
Recreation

Sneak Preview!

Over the next several weeks in our mathematics class, we will be developing proportion and percent skills, and collecting, organizing, and interpreting data while completing a thematic unit on Recreation. Some of the topics we will be discussing are:

▶ use of free time

▶ walking rates

▶ visits to zoos and amusement parks

▶ movie ratings

▶ sports activities

Ask Your Student

How can you estimate distances using your running rate? (Sec. 1)

How are audience approval ratings for movies determined? (Sec. 4)

How can an athlete's performance be predicted using statistics? (Sec. 5)

Connections

Literature:
Students will read an excerpt from *Zanboomer*, by R. R. Knudson. In the story, a high school student, Zan Hagen, takes up cross-country running. In the excerpt, her coach helps her train for a three-mile race. Your student might enjoy reading this book or others about young people training for sporting events.

Physical Education:
Running rates and basketball statistics are used to study percents and ratios. Your student may want to explore the statistics related to his or her other leisure time activities.

Science:
Students measure their resting and active heart rates and use a percent to compare the two measures.

E² Project

Following Section 2, students will have approximately one week to complete the Extended Exploration (E²), *What's for Lunch?* Students will use a map showing the paths in a zoo and a table showing feeding times for the animals to create possible tours for zoo visitors.

Module Project

After completing the module, students will gather and organize data about the ways students in their school spend their free time. Students will use percents and visual displays to present the results of their surveys.

Recreation

Section Title	Mathematics Students Will Be Learning	Activities
1: Run for Your Life	• using ratios, rates, and unit rates • setting up and solving proportions • choosing the best average • constructing and interpreting stem-and-leaf plots	• analyze running times • interpret race results
2: Water Adventure	• creating and conducting surveys • constructing and interpreting histograms	• create survey questions and conduct a survey • plan a water park
3: Just for Fun	• solving proportions by finding cross products • constructing scatter plots and drawing fitted lines • interpreting box-and-whisker plots	• explore the riders' experience on a roller coaster • examine the heights and speeds of roller coasters • examine stone-skipping data
4: You Be the Critic	• estimating percents • using a proportion to find what percent one number is of another • using a proportion to find a part of the whole amount or to find the whole amount when the percent is known	• analyze movie ratings and find audience approval ratings of movies or television shows
5: Make Every Shot Count	• writing fractions as decimals or percents • using "nice" fractions and mental math to estimate percents • using percents to make predictions • finding percents greater than 100%	• simulate shooting free throws to determine an average • analyze basketball statistics • find and compare resting and active heart rates

Activities to do at Home

• Plan a trip or family vacation using highway maps or flight information. Make a map to show possible routes, including stops, travel times, or distances. (After Sec. 2)

• Search for "roller coasters" on the internet and visit some of the sites to learn more about the design features—type of construction, height, drop, inversions, loops, etc.—and the physics of roller coasters. Then try one of the sites that lets you design your own roller coaster. (After Sec. 3)

• Look for rates, ratios, and percents around your home. You might want to explore gas and electric meters, food labels, the mail, newspapers, magazines, or television. (After Sec. 4)

Related Topics

You may want to discuss these related topics with your student:

 Participation in individual and team sports

 Entertainment

 Travel

Name _____ Problem _____

Teacher Assessment Scales
For use with Module 5

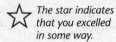 The star indicates that you excelled in some way.

 Problem Solving

❶ ❷ ❸ ❹ ❺

You did not understand the problem well enough to get started or you did not show any work.

You understood the problem well enough to make a plan and to work toward a solution.

You made a plan, you used it to solve the problem, and you verified your solution.

 Mathematical Language

❶ ❷ ❸ ❹ ❺

You did not use any mathematical vocabulary or symbols, or you did not use them correctly, or your use was not appropriate.

You used appropriate mathematical language, but the way it was used was not always correct or other terms and symbols were needed.

You used mathematical language that was correct and appropriate to make your meaning clear.

 Representations

❶ ❷ ❸ ❹ ❺

You did not use any representations such as equations, tables, graphs, or diagrams to help solve the problem or explain your solution.

You made appropriate representations to help solve the problem or help you explain your solution, but they were not always correct or other representations were needed.

You used appropriate and correct representations to solve the problem or explain your solution.

 Connections

❶ ❷ ❸ ❹ ❺

You attempted or solved the problem and then stopped.

You found patterns and used them to extend the solution to other cases, or you recognized that this problem relates to other problems, mathematical ideas, or applications.

You extended the ideas in the solution to the general case, or you showed how this problem relates to other problems, mathematical ideas, or applications.

 Presentation

❶ ❷ ❸ ❹ ❺

The presentation of your solution and reasoning is unclear to others.

The presentation of your solution and reasoning is clear in most places, but others may have trouble understanding parts of it.

The presentation of your solution and reasoning is clear and can be understood by others.

Content Used: _____

Notes on Errors: _____

_____

Computational Errors: Yes ☐ No ☐

Name _____   Problem _____

For use with Module 5

Problem Solving

① **②** **③** **④** **⑤**

I did not understand the problem well enough to get started or I did not show any work.

I understood the problem well enough to make a plan and to work toward a solution.

I made a plan, I used it to solve the problem, and I verified my solution.

Mathematical Language

① **②** **③** **④** **⑤**

I did not use any mathematical vocabulary or symbols, or I did not use them correctly, or my use was not appropriate.

I used appropriate mathematical language, but the way it was used was not always correct or other terms and symbols were needed.

I used mathematical language that was correct and appropriate to make my meaning clear.

Representations

① **②** **③** **④** **⑤**

I did not use any representations such as equations, tables, graphs, or diagrams to help solve the problem or explain my solution.

I made appropriate representations to help solve the problem or help me explain my solution, but they were not always correct or other representations were needed.

I used appropriate and correct representations to solve the problem or explain my solution.

Connections

① **②** **③** **④** **⑤**

I attempted or solved the problem and then stopped.

I found patterns and used them to extend the solution to other cases, or I recognized that this problem relates to other problems, mathematical ideas, or applications.

I extended the ideas in the solution to the general case, or I showed how this problem relates to other problems, mathematical ideas, or applications.

Presentation

① **②** **③** **④** **⑤**

The presentation of my solution and reasoning is unclear to others.

The presentation of my solution and reasoning is clear in most places, but others may have trouble understanding parts of it.

The presentation of my solution and reasoning is clear and can be understood by others.

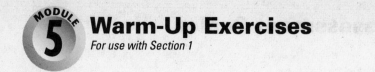

Warm-Up Exercises
For use with Section 1

Divide.

1. $45 \div 9$

2. $93 \div 6$

3. $22.8 \div 4$

Find the mean.

4. 1, 3, 6, 2, 3

5. 2.7, 3.4, 1.9, 4.6, 2.7, 3.9

ANSWERS

1. 5   2. 15.5   3. 5.7   4. 3   5. 3.2

Math Thematics, Book 2
Teacher's Resource Book, Modules 5 and 6

Name _____ Date _____

Practice and Applications

For use with Section 1

For use with Exploration 1

1. Write each rate as a unit rate.

a. $\dfrac{68 \text{ min}}{8 \text{ mi}}$ b. $\dfrac{138 \text{ mi}}{6 \text{ gal}}$ c. $\dfrac{\$8.40}{3 \text{ lb}}$

d. $\dfrac{48 \text{ servings}}{6 \text{ pans}}$ e. $\dfrac{\$0.28}{4 \text{ min}}$ f. $\dfrac{\$2.67}{3 \text{ bunches}}$

g. $\dfrac{32 \text{ min}}{5 \text{ mi}}$ h. $\dfrac{\$18}{4 \text{ lb}}$ i. $\dfrac{52.2 \text{ gal}}{9 \text{ min}}$

j. $\dfrac{30 \text{ servings}}{3 \text{ pans}}$ k. $\dfrac{\$7.77}{3 \text{ bunches}}$ l. $\dfrac{48 \text{ servings}}{4 \text{ pans}}$

m. $\dfrac{224 \text{ mi}}{8 \text{ gal}}$ n. $\dfrac{\$25.50}{2 \text{ hr}}$ o. $\dfrac{188 \text{ km}}{8 \text{ L}}$

2. A single grizzly bear may eat 55 pounds of berries per day. Copy and complete the proportion below to show how many pounds of berries a grizzly bear may eat in one week.

$$\dfrac{55 \text{ lb}}{1 \text{ day}} = \dfrac{? \text{ lb}}{7 \text{ days}}$$

3. The total area of Washington, D.C. is about 68 mi^2. The total population of Washington, D.C. is about 600,000 people. Find the population density, or unit rate of people per square mile, for Washington, D.C.

4. To train for a cross country ski race, Frank wants to ski a total of 120 mi at an average rate no slower than 8 min/mi.

a. Copy and complete the table below to show the distance covered and cross country skiing times for a rate of 8 min/mi.

Time (min)	?	8	?	80	?
Distance (mi)	0.5	1	5	?	120

b. How many hours would it take Frank to cross country ski 120 mi at a rate of 8 min/mi?

5. Suppose Erin runs at the rates shown in the table below.

a. Copy and complete the table for 30 sec and 50 sec.

Time (sec)	1	5	20	30	50
Distance (ft)	6	30	120	?	?

b. How far would you expect Erin to run in 50 sec?

(continued)

Name _____   Date _____

Practice and Applications
For use with Section 1

For use with Exploration 2

6. The table shows the number of minutes 20 students in Mr. Clement's class spent reading one night.

Student	Number of minutes	Student	Number of minutes
Jim	89	Doreen	94
Tim	76	Mary	88
Ralph	100	Bob	83
Keisha	85	Nick	79
Arnold	92	Matt	91
Barney	99	Liza	100
Alicia	89	Marty	89
Francine	88	Rosa	86
Buster	83	Janice	92
Arthur	90	Carter	96

a. Make a stem-and-leaf plot to show the number of minutes the students in Mr. Clement's class spent reading one night. Be sure to include a title and a key for your plot.

b. Use the stem-and-leaf plot to find the range, the mean, the median, and the mode of the number of minutes the students in Mr. Clement's class spent reading.

c. What would you consider to be the average number of minutes the students in Mr. Clement's class spent reading?

7. The stem-and-leaf plot shows the number of minutes 20 students in Mr. Clement's class spent studying for a test the following night.

a. Find the median and the mode(s) of the data.

b. Do you notice any gaps or clusters in the data? Explain.

c. Suppose one more student were included in the data and this student spent 51 minutes studying. How does this number affect the range of the data set? Explain.

Number of Minutes Spent Studying

```
1 | 8
2 | 0 5 5 5 6 9
3 | 2 4 7
4 | 6 8 8 8
5 |
6 | 0 5
7 | 2 3 6
8 | 3
```

4 | 8 = 48 minutes

Math Thematics, Book 2
Teacher's Resource Book, Modules 5 and 6

Study Guide
For use with Section 1

Run for Your Life   Ratios and Data Displays

GOAL   **LEARN HOW TO:** • find unit rates
                    • set up proportions
                    • interpret and make stem-and-leaf plots

AS YOU: • explore running times
              • examine race results

Exploration 1: Ratios and Proportions

Ratios, Rates, and Proportions

A **ratio** is a comparison of two quantities by division. A ratio can be written in any of the three forms shown at the right.

12 ft to 3 sec $\dfrac{12\ \text{ft}}{3\ \text{sec}}$ 12 ft : 3 sec

A **rate** is a ratio that compares quantities measured in different units.

Examples
a. The ratio $\dfrac{35\ \text{mi}}{2\ \text{gal}}$ compares miles to gallons by division, so it is a rate.
b. The ratio $\dfrac{3\ \text{min}}{60\ \text{min}}$ compares minutes to minutes, so it is *not* a rate.

A **proportion** is an equation stating that two ratios are equivalent. A **unit rate** is the rate for one unit of a given quantity.

Example
Write $\dfrac{\$4.50}{6\ \text{cans}}$ as a unit rate.

Sample Response

Use a proportion to find the unit rate; that is, find the price for just 1 can.

$$\dfrac{\$4.50}{6\ \text{cans}} = \dfrac{x}{1\ \text{can}}$$

Think: What number must you divide the numerator and denominator by to change 6 cans to 1 can?

$$\dfrac{\$4.50 \div 6}{6\ \text{cans} \div 6} = \dfrac{\$0.75}{1\ \text{can}}$$

The unit rate is $0.75/can.

Study Guide
For use with Section 1

Exploration 2: Stem-and-Leaf Plots

Displays of Data

The **median** is the middle item when you order a data set from least to greatest. The **mode** is the item or the items that appear most often in a set of data. The **range** of a data set is the difference between the greatest data value and the least data value.

Stem-and-leaf plots can be used to organize and display data. Stem-and-leaf plots show each data value. The stems are written vertically in order from least to greatest. The leaves are then written horizontally next to the appropriate stem in order from least to greatest.

A stem-and-leaf plot should always include a key. The key shows which place value each digit represents.

Medals Won by the Top 20 Countries in 1996 Olympics

```
 1  | 5 5 5 5 7 7 9
 2  | 0 1 2 3 5 7
 3  | 5 7
 4  | 1
 5  | 0
 6  | 3 5
 7  |
 8  |
 9  |
10  | 1
```

6 | 3 represents 63 medals.

> #### Example
>
> Find the mode, the median, and the range of the data shown in the stem-and-leaf plot above.
>
> #### Sample Response
>
> The mode is 15, because 15 occurs most often (4 times).
>
> There are 20 data values in order in the plot. The median is the average of the 10th and 11th values found by counting from the first row of the plot. So, the median is $(22 + 23) \div 2$, or 22.5.
>
> The greatest value is 101 and the least value is 15, so the range is $101 - 15$, or 86.

A *cluster* in a data set is a group of data values that are close in value.
A *gap* in a data set is a place where there is a "jump" between data values.

> #### Example
>
> Are there any gaps or clusters in the data shown in the stem-and-leaf plot above? Explain.
>
> #### Sample Response
>
> Yes, there is a gap between the values 65 and 101 because no data exists between these values. There is a cluster around the value 15 (the mode of the data).

Name _____ Date _____

Study Guide: Practice & Application Exercises

For use with Section 1

5-13

Exploration 1

For Exercises 1–4, write each rate as a unit rate.

1. $\dfrac{\$13.80}{3 \text{ boxes}}$

2. $\dfrac{135 \text{ mi}}{5 \text{ gal}}$

3. $\dfrac{25¢}{4 \text{ min}}$

4. $\dfrac{3 \text{ mi}}{25 \text{ min}}$

5. Xavier can read 80 words per minute. Write the ratio that expresses Xavier's reading pace three different ways.

6. A produce sign had the ratios $\dfrac{\$3}{\text{lb}}$, $\dfrac{\$0.95}{\text{oz}}$, and $\dfrac{\$2.50}{2 \text{ kg}}$ on its price list. Which ratio is *not* a unit rate? Explain.

7. A typical shower uses 4 gal of water per minute. How many gallons of water are used during a 15 min shower?

8. Long distance company X charges $2.70 for a 15 min call. Company Y charges $4.50 for a 27 min call. Which phone company has the best rates for its customers?

Exploration 2

9. This list below shows the ages of students enrolled in art classes at a local museum.

   15, 23, 18, 45, 63, 70, 34, 15, 28, 65, 65, 67, 19

   a. Make a stem-and-leaf plot to show the ages of the students. Be sure to include a title and a key for your plot.

   b. Use the stem-and-leaf plot to find the range, the median, and the mode of the data.

   c. Are any of the ages unusually young or old in comparison to the ages of other people enrolled in the art class? Explain.

   d. Suppose two more people, ages 14 and 15, enrolled in the art class. How would these numbers affect the range of the data? the mode?

Quick Quiz
For use after Section 1

1. Write $\dfrac{\$14.50}{3\,\text{lb}}$ as a unit rate.

2. At 65 mi/hr, how long will it take to drive 442 mi?

3. Find the range, median, and the mode.

   Point Differences of First 20 Super Bowls

   ```
   0 | 3 4 4 5 7 9
   1 | 0 0 2 6 7 7 7 8 9
   2 | 1 2 5 9
   3 | 6
   ```

   1 | 2 represents 12 points

4. A set of fifteen test scores has a range of 31 with clusters in the mid 70s and low 90s. Design a stem-and-leaf plot of fifteen possible scores so that the median score is 84.

Name _____   Date _____

Warm-Up Exercises
For use with Section 2

5-15

Listed are the ages at which the last 10 U.S. presidents of the 20th century took office: 60, 62, 43, 55, 56, 61, 52, 69, 64, 46. Use this data for Exercises 1–4.

1. Create a stem-and-leaf plot of the ages at which the last 10 presidents of the 20th century took office.

2. What is the median age of the presidents?

3. What is the mode?

4. What is the range of the ages?

ANSWERS

1. 4│3 6   2. 58   3. none   4. 26 years
   5│2 5 6
   6│0 1 2 4 9

     5 | 6 represents 56 years old

Name _____ Date _____

United States Outdoor Water Parks Admission Fees

(Use with Question 9 on page 333.)

Selected United States Water Parks 2005 Admission Fees			
Water Park	**Location**	**Adult**	**Junior**
Big Surf	Tempe, AZ	$ 21.00	$ 17.00
Blizzard Beach	Orlando, FL	31.75	25.44
Four Bears	Utica, MI	12.95	5.95
Great Waves	Alexandria, VA	10.50	8.50
Hurricane Harbor	Arlington, TX	29.99	19.99
Hurricane Harbor	Chicago, IL	44.99	29.99
Hurricane Harbor	Los Angeles, CA	23.99	16.99
Knight's Caribbean Water Adventure	Springfield, IL	19.95	15.95
Noah's Ark	Wisconsin Dells, WI	28.99	15.99
Raging Waters	Grafton, IL	17.95	14.95
Raging Waters	Salt Lake City, UT	17.95	13.95
Raging Waters	San Dimas, CA	27.99	16.99
Raging Waters	San Jose, CA	25.99	19.99
Schlitterbahn	New Braufels, TX	29.95	24.84
Seven Peaks	Provo, UT	18.50	14.50
Shipwreck Island	Panama Beach, FL	27.00	22.00
Soak City	Buena Park, CA	26.95	13.95
Splashtown	Houston, TX	29.99	19.99
Splashwater Kingdom	Lake George, NY	35.99	19.99
Splish Splash	Long Island, NY	26.99	19.99
Typhoon Lagoon	Orlando, FL	31.75	25.44
Water Country USA	Williamsburg, VA	31.99	24.99
Water Safari	Old Forge, NY	23.95	19.95
Waterville USA	Gulf Shore, AL	25.00	17.00
Waterworld	Denver, CO	24.95	20.95
Waterworld	Wisconsin Dells, WI	14.75	14.75
Waterworld Safari	Phoenix, AZ	21.00	17.00
Wet 'n Wild	El Paso, TX	17.95	15.95
Wet 'n Wild	Las Vegas, NV	27.99	15.99
White Water	Atlanta, GA	31.99	19.99
White Water Bay	Oklahoma City, OK	22.99	17.99
Wild Mountain Water Park	Taylors Falls, MN	14.56	9.39
Wild Rivers	Irvine, CA	27.98	17.98
Wild Waves	Federal Way, WA	31.99	31.99
Wyandot Lake	Columbus, OH	25.99	19.99

Math Thematics, Book 2
Teacher's Resource Book, Modules 5 and 6

MODULE 5   **LABSHEET** 2B

Histogram (Use with Questions 11–15 on pages 333–334.)

Directions

a. Find the number of admission fees in each price range on the stem-and-leaf plot you built in Question 9.

b. Use the frequencies to decide on a vertical scale for your graph. Add your vertical scale to the graph.

c. Draw bars on the graph to show the number of admission fees in each price range. Each bar should be the width of the interval with no space between bars.

d. Label the horizontal and vertical axes of the graph.

2005 U.S. Water Park Admission Fees

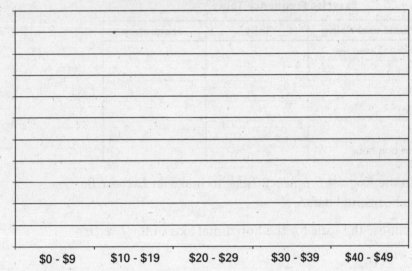

$0 - $9 $10 - $19 $20 - $29 $30 - $39 $40 - $49

Name _____ Date _____

Practice and Applications
For use with Section 2

For use with Exploration 1

1. What is the letter of the phrase that best represents the average amount of time you spent each day last year exercising?

   A. did not usually exercise   **B.** 20 minutes   **C.** 30 minutes

   D. 45 minutes   **E.** one hour   **F.** more than one hour

2. Use a frequency table like the one shown below to survey classmates, friends, or relatives for the question in Exercise 1.

   Exercise Frequency Table

Time spent exercising	Tally	Frequency
usually did not exercise		
20 minutes		
30 minutes		
45 minutes		
one hour		
more than one hour		

3. Use the data in the *Exercise Frequency Table* to make an *Exercise Bar Graph* that has horizontal bars.

4. How did you choose the scale for the horizontal axis of the *Exercise Bar Graph*?

5. How did you find the most frequent answer to Exercise 1 from the *Exercise Frequency Table*? from the *Exercise Bar Graph*?

6. How is your *Exercise Bar Graph* like the bar graph shown below?

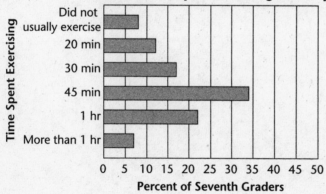

(continued)

Name _____ Date _____

Practice and Applications

For use with Section 2

For use with Exploration 2

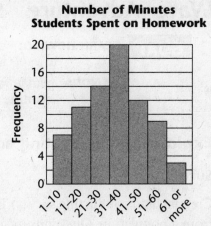

Number of Minutes Students Spent on Homework

7. The histogram shows the number of minutes students spent on their homework at Alta Junior High School.

   a. How many minutes are included in each interval?

   b. About how many students spend from 21–30 minutes on homework?

   c. Is the number of students who spend more than one half hour on homework *greater than*, *equal to*, or *less than* the number of students who spend less than one half hour on homework?

   d. Can you determine the number of students who spent exactly 40 minutes on homework? Explain.

8. An organization is considering plans for a new playground and took a community survey. The frequency table below indicates the numbers of children from different age groups living in the community.

Children Living in Maple Grove	
Age Group	**Frequency**
1–3	12
4–6	18
7–9	29
10–12	14

   a. Would you display the results using a bar graph or a histogram? Explain.

   b. How might the survey results be used by the community organization?

Study Guide
For use with Section 2

Water Adventure   Surveys and Data Displays

GOAL   **LEARN HOW TO:** • create and conduct a survey
• interpret histograms

AS YOU: • plan a water park
• examine admission fees at U.S. water parks

Exploration 1: Creating and Conducting Surveys

Surveys

Creating and conducting surveys is a method of gathering information from a population. Questions included in a survey should provide enough information to make good decisions about an issue.

Using Frequency Tables

Frequency tables show how often each data item in a survey occurs. The frequency table at the right shows the number of students in four middle school classes who take work home. The total number of tally marks in each category is the **frequency** for that category.

Number of Students Taking Work Home

Day	Tally	Frequency
Monday	~~IIII~~ ~~IIII~~ ~~IIII~~ ~~IIII~~ ~~IIII~~	25
Tuesday	~~IIII~~ ~~IIII~~ IIII	15
Wednesday	~~IIII~~ ~~IIII~~ ~~IIII~~ IIII	19
Thursday	~~IIII~~ ~~IIII~~ ~~IIII~~ ~~IIII~~ ~~IIII~~ III	28
Friday	IIII	4

Example

Refer to the frequency table above. Make a bar graph of the survey data given in the frequency table.

Sample Response

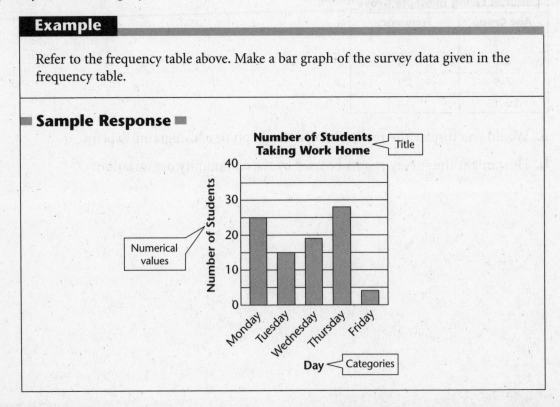

Name _____ Date _____

Exploration 2: Histograms

Frequency tables and **histograms** display frequencies in given intervals. A histogram is a bar graph with no spaces between the bars. Histograms display grouped data.

Weight of Puppies Sold at a Pet Store	
Weight (lb)	**Frequency**
0.1–2.0	23
2.1–4.0	25
4.1–6.0	15
6.1–8.0	9
8.1–10.0	5

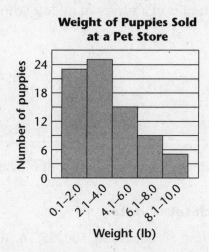

Example

The frequency table shows the results of a school survey.

Favorite Sport	
Sport	**Frequency**
baseball	36
basketball	42
soccer	29
swimming	30
tennis	17

Which is the best way to display the data in the frequency table, a bar graph or a histogram?

■ Sample Response ■

A bar graph is best because the data are grouped by category. Histograms are best used when data are grouped in intervals.

Math Thematics, Book 2

Name _____ Date _____

Study Guide: Practice & Application Exercises

For use with Section 2

Exploration 1

1. Andrea would like to open a new café at the library. Write a survey of 4 questions that will provide Andrea with good information before she opens the café.

2. The frequency table shows the results of a survey of middle school students.

Favorite Type of Movie	
Type of Movie	Frequency
cartoon	22
adventure	48
science fiction	20
comedy	49

   Can you tell from this survey which is the favorite type of movie among middle school students? Explain.

Make a frequency table for each set of data.

3. Scores on an English grammar test: 88, 88, 76, 98, 100, 95, 76, 100, 85, 98, 88, 85, 76, 79, 75, 88, 91, 93, 71, 65, 88, 93, 65, 85

4. Favorite color of cross country team members: blue, red, yellow, yellow, red, green, green, orange, blue, blue, green, yellow, red

Exploration 2

Use the histogram at the right.

5. Is the number of students who read more than 3 hours per week *greater than, equal to*, or *less than* the number of students who read 3 hours or less per week?

6. How many students read at least 2 hours each week?

7. Can you tell the mode number of hours students spent reading by looking at the histogram? Explain.

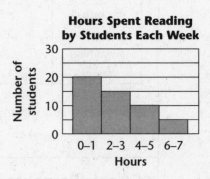

Hours Spent Reading by Students Each Week

Quick Quiz
For use after Section 2

Use the results of the survey of 70 students as shown in the frequency table at the right for Exercises 1 and 2.

Favorite Subject	Frequency
mathematics	28
science	11
English	17
social studies	14

1. Write a survey question that students may have been asked to get these results.

2. Make a graph that would best display the data from the survey.

3. Make a frequency table for this set of data about the number of CDs bought in the past month: 2, 0, 6, 1, 2, 5, 0, 1, 1, 0, 4, 3, 2, 1, 12, 2, 4, 3

4. Use the histogram at the right to find how many students scored between 70 and 89 on the math exam.

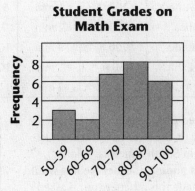

Student Grades on Math Exam

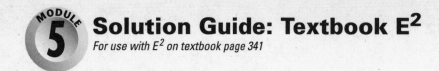

Solution Guide: Textbook E²

For use with E² on textbook page 341

What's for Lunch?

The Problem Solving, Representations, and Presentation Scales of the *Math Thematics Assessment Scales* should be used to assess student work. This E² has several solutions (possible tours). Students may visit as few as two animal feedings or up to five. When evaluating students' tours, check that all conditions have been met, the amount of time is included, and all assumptions are clearly stated.

The sample response below shows part of a student's solution.

Partial Solution

I wanted to visit exhibits that included an animal feeding and also see a variety of animals. I saw that the macaques would be fed at 9 A.M. in Eurasia and Eurasia is close to the play area, so I planned to go there first. South America has a llama feeding at 9:30 A.M., so I went there next. In Africa they feed the hippopotamus at 10:00 A.M. and it is close to South America, so I planned to go there next. Since the next feedings weren't until 11 A.M. I decided to show the visitors some other exhibits, so we went to Australia and the Emu Exhibit. I also wanted to see the polar bear feeding at 11:30 A.M.

The table and map below show the route I chose, the areas visited, the amount of time, and the distance traveled on this tour. To find the walking rate, I timed my parents walking along 50 ft of sidewalk. They walked this distance 6 times in 1 minute. This gave me a rate of 300 ft/min. In the table, all times were rounded to the next minute.

Area	Distance traveled to reach this area	Time to travel to this area	Start time	Animal to be fed	Animal feeding time	End time	Total distance traveled
Play Area	0	0	8:45 A.M.	none		8:50 A.M.	0
Eurasia	200 ft	1 min	8:51 A.M.	macaques	9:00–9:20 A.M.	9:21 A.M.	200 ft
South America	200 ft	1 min	9:22 A.M.	llama	9:30–9:50 A.M.	9:53 A.M.	400 ft
Africa	500 ft	2 min	9:55 A.M.	hippopotamus	10:00–10:20 A.M.	10:25 A.M.	900 ft
Australia	900 ft	3 min	10:28 A.M.	none		10:58 A.M.	1800 ft
Emu Exhibit	50 ft	1 min	10:59 A.M.	none		11:20 A.M.	1850 ft
North America	375 ft	2 min	11:22 A.M.	polar bear	11:30–11:50 A.M.	noon	2225 ft

I realized that I could have included a feeding of the tiger in Eurasia or the jaguar in South America. I don't know if adding another feeding would have made this a better tour. I asked my friends and family and they thought they'd like to see the emus since they didn't know what they were, rather than see the tiger or jaguar fed.

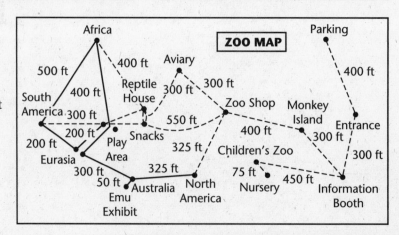

Warm-Up Exercises

For use with Section 3

Complete each proportion.

1. $\dfrac{2}{1} = \dfrac{6}{?}$

2. $\dfrac{?}{8} = \dfrac{3}{1}$

3. $\dfrac{125}{25} = \dfrac{?}{1}$

Write in lowest terms.

4. $\dfrac{39}{52}$

5. $\dfrac{21}{49}$

ANSWERS

1. 3   2. 24   3. 5   4. $\frac{3}{4}$ 5. $\frac{3}{7}$

| MODULE 5 | LABSHEET 3A |

Steel Roller Coaster Data (Use with Questions 16, 17, and 19 on pages 346–347.)

Height and Speed of Select U.S. Steel Roller Coasters			
Name	**Amusement Park**	**Height (ft)**	**Maximum Speed (mi/hr)**
Anaconda	Paramount King's Dominion	128	50
Big Coaster	Wonderland Amusement Park	55	35
California Screamin'	Disney's California Adventure	120	55
Corkscrew	Playland Amusement Park	75	40
Desperado	Buffalo Bill's Hotel and Casino	209	80
Excalibar	Valleyfair	105	54
Gauntlet	Magic Springs	109	50
Goliath	Six Flags Magic Mountain	235	85
Iron Wolf	Six Flags Great America	100	55
Kingda Ka	Six Flags Great Adventure	456	128
Mantis	Cedar Point	145	57
Medusa	Six Flags Great Adventure	142	61
Millennium Force	Cedar Point	310	92
Montu	Busch Gardens	150	60
Phantom's Revenge	Kennywood	160	82
Raptor	Cedar Point	137	57
Scorpion	Busch Gardens	65	50
Storm Runner	Hersheypark	150	70
Superman Ride of Steel	Six Flags America	190	73
Superman, the Escape	Six Flags Magic Mountain	415	100
Texas Tornado	Wonderland Amusement Park	80	50
Titan	Six Flags Over Texas	245	85
Top Thrill Dragster	Cedar Point	420	120
Whizzer	Six Flags Great America	70	42
Xcelerator	Knott's Berry Farm	205	82

Math Thematics, Book 2
Teacher's Resource Book, Modules 5 and 6

MODULE 5   **LABSHEET 3B**   **5-27**

Wooden Roller Coaster Scatter Plot (Use with Questions 18–22 on pages 346–347.)

Select Wooden Roller Coasters in U.S. Amusement Parks

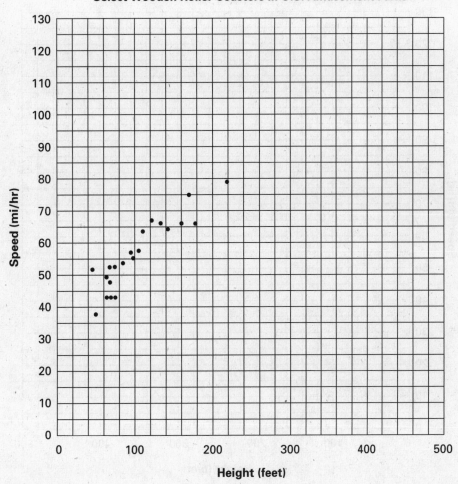

MODULE 5   **LABSHEET** 3C

Steel Roller Coaster Scatter Plot (Use with Questions 18–22 on pages 346–347.)

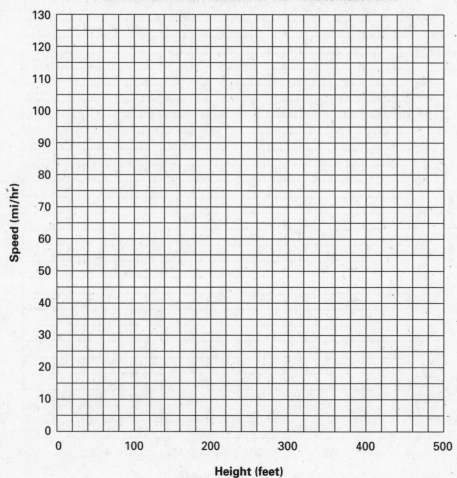

Select Steel Roller Coasters in U.S. Amusement Parks

MODULE 5   **LABSHEET** **3D**   **5-29**

Box-and-Whisker Plot (Use with Questions 24–29 on pages 348–349.)

Directions Plot the winning number of skips for each year on the line plot below the box-and-whisker plot. The first three values in the table have been plotted for you.

Mackinac Island Stone Skipping Tournament 1970–2006

Year	Winning number of skips	Year	Winning number of skips
1970	13 ✔	1985–1991	(not available)
1971	13 ✔	1992	18
1972	10 ✔	1993	13
1973	9	1994	13
1974	19	1995	16
1975	24	1996	18
1976	23	1997	(not available)
1977	24	1998	(not available)
1978	18	1999	22
1979	17	2000	23
1980	15	2001	24
1981	(not available)	2002	20
1982	22	2003	24
1983	15	2004	21
1984	20	2005	30
		2006	25

Mackinac Island Stone Skipping Tournament 1970–2006*

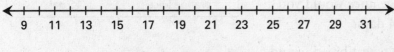

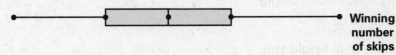

Winning number of skips

*except 1981, 1985–1991, 1997, and 1998

Practice and Applications

For use with Section 3

For use with Exploration 1

1. How many grams of protein are contained in 680 g of yogurt if 170 g of yogurt contain 7 g of protein?

2. How many grams of carbohydrate are contained in 448 g of pasta if 56 g of pasta contain 40 g of carbohydrate?

3. A horse eats about 75 lb of hay every 4 days. How many pounds of hay would you expect it to eat in 28 days?

4. Solve each proportion.

   a. $\dfrac{8}{15} = \dfrac{28}{x}$　　b. $\dfrac{7}{n} = \dfrac{112}{384}$　　c. $\dfrac{12}{76} = \dfrac{b}{171}$

   d. $\dfrac{36}{45} = \dfrac{y}{15}$　　e. $\dfrac{m}{24} = \dfrac{51}{72}$　　f. $\dfrac{3}{x} = \dfrac{24}{40}$

   g. $\dfrac{5}{12} = \dfrac{w}{30}$　　h. $\dfrac{16}{c} = \dfrac{56}{105}$　　i. $\dfrac{5}{9} = \dfrac{4.5}{t}$

   j. $\dfrac{4.5}{x} = \dfrac{18}{48}$　　k. $\dfrac{5}{9} = \dfrac{z}{72}$　　l. $\dfrac{14}{k} = \dfrac{56}{34}$

   m. $\dfrac{4}{18} = \dfrac{10}{x}$　　n. $\dfrac{8}{14} = \dfrac{12}{n}$　　o. $\dfrac{9}{15} = \dfrac{b}{75}$

5. A selection of the Morningside Café's breakfast menu is shown at the right with the average quantity of the items the restaurant usually uses in two days.

   a. How many pounds of pancake mix would you expect the Morningside Café to use in 7 days?

   b. How many gallons of orange juice would you expect the Café to use in 14 days?

   c. How many loaves of whole wheat bread would you expect the Café to use in 30 days?

   d. How many pounds of maple syrup would you expect the Café to use in 60 days?

Morningside Café Breakfast Menu

Item	Amount
bacon	35 lb
eggs	40 dozen
whole wheat bread	50 loaves
white bread	85 loaves
pancake mix	75 lb
maple syrup	12 lb
orange juice	15 gal

(continued)

Name _____   Date _____

Practice and Applications
For use with Section 3

For use with Exploration 2

6. Two real estate agents made the scatter plots below to show the relationship between the living area and selling prices of houses in a selected area. Choose the letter of the scatter plot that you think shows the better fitted line. Explain your choice.

A.
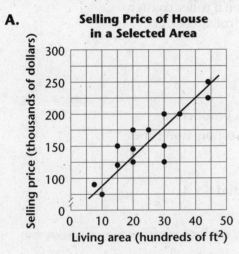

B.
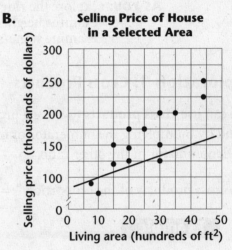

7. Use the scatter plot you chose in Exercise 6.

   a. About what do you think the selling price of a 3500 ft^2 house in the selected area would be?

   b. There are two houses with a living area of 3000 ft^2. One sells for $125,000 and the other sells for $150,000. Why do you think the selling prices are different?

For use with Exploration 3

8. Use the box-and-whisker plot shown.

   a. Estimate the greatest amount of money a shopper spent at the grocery store.

   b. Estimate the least amount of money a shopper spent at the grocery store.

   c. Estimate the median amount of money a shopper spent at the grocery store.

   d. Estimate the range in the amounts of money the shoppers spent at the grocery store.

**Amount of Money Spent
by 75 Shoppers in a Grocery Store**

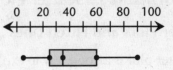

Name _____ Date _____

Study Guide
For use with Section 3

Just for Fun   Proportions and Plots

GOAL   **LEARN HOW TO:** • solve proportions using cross products
• make a scatter plot
• fit a line to a scatter plot
• interpret box-and-whisker plots

AS YOU: • explore the riders' experience on a roller coaster
• examine heights and speeds of roller coasters
• examine stone-skipping data

Exploration 1: Cross Products

You can use **cross products** to solve a proportion. Cross products are found by multiplying the numerator of one ratio in the proportion times the denominator of the other ratio.

The cross products of the proportion $\frac{1}{3} = \frac{4}{12}$ are $1 \cdot 12$ and $3 \cdot 4$.

Example

Solve the proportion $\frac{4}{5} = \frac{x}{15}$.

■ Sample Response ■

$$\frac{4}{5} = \frac{x}{15}$$

$4 \cdot 15 = 5 \cdot x$ ← Use cross products to write an equation.

$60 = 5x$

$\frac{60}{5} = \frac{5x}{5}$ ← Divide both sides by 5.

$12 = x$

Exploration 2: Scatter Plots

Scatter Plots and Fitted Lines

A **scatter plot** is a good way to explore how two sets of data are related. If the data values lie along a line, you can use a **fitted line** to make predictions.

For example, the fitted line on the scatter plot at the right can be used to predict that about 25 trees will be sold at $125 each.

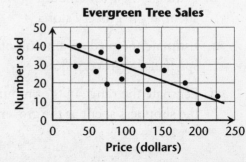

Evergreen Tree Sales

Study Guide

For use with Section 3

Exploration 3: Box-and-Whisker Plots

Box-and-whisker plots are useful for displaying a set of data.
A box-and-whisker plot divides the data values into four groups.

- The whisker on the left is called the *lower whisker*. The dot at the left
  end of the lower whisker represents the least value.

- The whisker on the right is the *upper whisker* and the dot at its right
  end represents the greatest value.

- The box represents the middle data values. It is divided into two
  parts—the *lower portion of the box* and the *upper portion of the box*.

- The box between the two whiskers is divided into two parts by a
  vertical line. This vertical line represents the *median of the entire
  data set* (50% of the data are less than this value and 50% are greater).

Also, each of the whiskers and each part of the box
contain approximately 25% of the values in the data set.

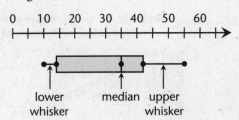

Example

Refer to the box-and-whisker plot above.

a. What is the greatest data value of the data set? the least data value?

b. What is the range of the data?

c. What is the median of the data?

d. About what percent of the data are greater than 14?

▬ Sample Response ▬

a. 55 (The value represented by the right end of the upper whisker.); 10 (The value
represented by the left end of the lower whisker.)

b. 55 – 10, or 45

c. 35

d. Since 14 is the value represented by the lower end of the box, approximately 75%
of the data values are greater than 14.

Name _____   Date _____

Study Guide: Practice & Application Exercises
For use with Section 3

Exploration 1

Solve each proportion.

1. $\frac{8}{22} = \frac{g}{33}$ **2.** $\frac{4}{k} = \frac{6}{21}$ **3.** $\frac{18}{24} = \frac{c}{40}$ **4.** $\frac{5}{12} = \frac{3.5}{x}$

5. Ingrid feeds her dog 28 oz of food each day. How many ounces of food are needed to feed her dog for 7 days?

6. If 4 cans of dog food cost $1.50, how much will 10 cans of dog food cost?

Exploration 2

The scatter plots below show the relationship between the monthly normal temperatures and the average precipitation for Boston, Massachusetts.

A. **Monthly Normal Temperatures/Precipitation in Boston, MA**

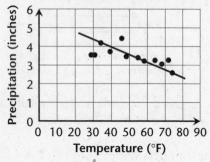

B. **Monthly Normal Temperatures/Precipitation in Boston, MA**

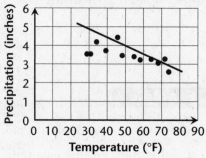

7. Choose the letter of the scatter plot that you think shows the better fitted line. Explain your choice.

8. About how many inches of precipitation would you expect in Boston when the temperature averages 50°F?

Exploration 3

Use the box-and-whisker plot at the right.

9. What is the age of the youngest swimmer?

10. About half of the swimmers are under what age?

11. What is the range of ages of the swimmers?

12. There are 20 members of the swim team. About how many members are more than 8 years old?

Age of Swim Team Members (years)

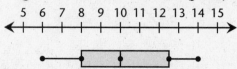

Name _____ Date _____

Quick Quiz
For use after Section 3

1. If there are 8 slices in one pizza, how many slices are there in 13 pizzas?

2. Solve the proportion $\frac{9}{15} = \frac{x}{70}$.

3. Use graph paper to make a scatter plot of the data at the right.

4. Use your scatter plot in Question 3 to estimate the winning time for the year 2020.

Winning Distances for Men's Olympic Discus

Year	Distance (ft)
1900	118
1920	147
1936	166
1960	194
1980	219
2000	227

5. The box-and-whisker plot shows data for a frog-jumping contest.

    a. What is the range of jumps?

    b. What is the median jump?

Jump Lengths (ft)

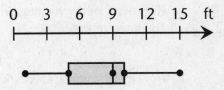

Name _____ Date _____

Write each rate as a unit rate.

1. $\dfrac{\$18}{4.5\ lb}$

2. $\dfrac{0.2\ in.}{50\ min}$

3. The numbers of home runs hit by Triple Crown winners the year they won the Triple Crown are 14, 31, 28, 39, 42, 18, 44, 49, 52, 32, 36, 49, 48, 9, 14.

   a. Make a stem-and-leaf plot using the home run data.

   b. Find the range, median, and mode(s) of the data.

     range = _____ median = _____ mode(s) = _____

4. The histogram shows average speeds of the winning drivers in the Indianapolis 500, 1957–2007.

   a. How many of the winning drivers drove 160 mi/hr or faster?

   b. How many winning speeds were between 140 mi/hr and 159 mi/hr?

   c. Can you tell what the fastest winning speed was? Explain.

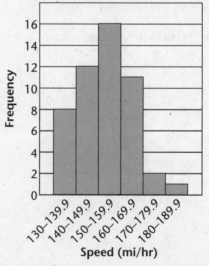

Race Speed of Winning Drivers in the Indianapolis 500, 1957–2007

Solve each proportion.

5. $\dfrac{2}{x} = \dfrac{9}{26}$

6. $\dfrac{x}{80} = \dfrac{42}{140}$

(continued)

Mid-Module Quiz

For use after Section 3

7. a. Make a scatter plot for the data in the table.

Winning Distance for Men's Olympic Triple Jump

Year	Distance (rounded to nearest ft)
1900	47
1920	48
1936	52
1960	55
1980	57
2000	58
2020	?

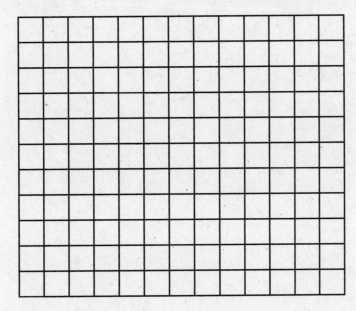

b. Draw a fitted line for your scatter plot.

c. Predict the winning distance in the triple jump for the 2020 Olympics.

8. The box-and-whisker plot shows the number of moves made in a series of games of Tic-Tac-Toe.

a. What is the median number of moves?

b. What is the range?

Number of Moves in Tic-Tac-Toe

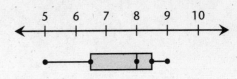

Name _____ Date _____

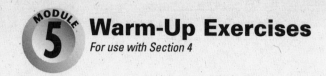

Warm-Up Exercises
For use with Section 4

Convert each fraction to a percent.

1. $\dfrac{1}{4}$

2. $\dfrac{1}{10}$

3. $\dfrac{1}{2}$

Solve each proportion.

4. $\dfrac{x}{100} = \dfrac{14}{40}$

5. $\dfrac{32}{100} = \dfrac{50}{x}$

ANSWERS

1. 25%   2. 10%   3. 50%   4. 35   5. 156.25

Name _____ Date _____

| **MODULE 5** | **LABSHEET** 4A |

Estimating Percents (Use with Question 6 on page 359.)

Directions Complete the exercises below to estimate the percent equivalent of the fraction $\frac{17}{30}$.

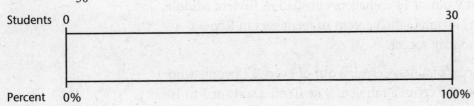

Students 0   30

Percent   0%   100%

   a. Use vertical segments to divide the bar into five sections of equal length.

   b. What "nice" fractions do the vertical segments you drew in part (a) represent?

   c. Below the bar, write the percent that each vertical segment represents.

   d. Across the top of the bar, write the number of students represented by each vertical assignment.

   e. Draw a segment about where you think 17 students should be located on the percent bar model. Shade the bar from 0 to 17.

   f. Estimate the percent equivalent of $\frac{17}{30}$.

Practice and Applications

For use with Section 4

For use with Exploration 1

1. It is estimated that 9 out of 14 teenagers enrolled in Riviera Middle School play soccer. Estimate the percent of teenagers in Riviera Middle School who play soccer.

2. In a marketing survey of a new cereal, 8 out of every 17 people who responded gave the new cereal a rating of 9 or 10 on a scale of 1 to 10.

   a. What "nice" fraction can you use to estimate the percent of people who gave the cereal a rating of 9 or 10?

   b. Estimate the percent of people who gave the cereal a rating of 9 or 10.

3. Estimate the percent equivalent of each ratio.

   a. $\dfrac{9}{11}$ b. $\dfrac{11}{32}$ c. $\dfrac{7}{18}$

   d. $\dfrac{24}{35}$ e. $\dfrac{10}{24}$ f. $\dfrac{42}{85}$

   g. $\dfrac{17}{21}$ h. $\dfrac{42}{98}$ i. $\dfrac{34}{99}$

   j. $\dfrac{4}{19}$ k. $\dfrac{6}{49}$ l. $\dfrac{11}{45}$

For use with Exploration 2

4. Set up and solve a proportion to find the actual percent for Exercises 1 and 2. Round each answer to the nearest percent.

5. Write each ratio as a percent. Round to the nearest tenth.

   a. $\dfrac{10}{12}$ b. $\dfrac{54}{135}$ c. $\dfrac{72}{96}$

   d. $\dfrac{75}{120}$ e. $\dfrac{21}{30}$ f. $\dfrac{45}{96}$

   g. $\dfrac{40}{150}$ h. $\dfrac{52}{160}$ i. $\dfrac{12}{72}$

   j. $\dfrac{28}{36}$ k. $\dfrac{25}{80}$ l. $\dfrac{14}{70}$

6. Of the 2628 new books purchased by the library, 525 were for teenagers. What percent of the new books were for teenagers?

(continued)

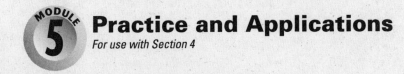

Practice and Applications
For use with Section 4

For use with Exploration 3

7. Suppose 44% of students at a school do not like classical music. If 198 students do not like classical music, how many students are there in the school? Explain your reasoning.

8. Find each unknown number.

a. 35% of a number is 17.5.　　　　**b.** 42 is 70% of a number.

c. 68% of a number is 578.　　　　**d.** A number is 34% of 75.

e. 18% of a number is 32.4.　　　　**f.** A number is 23% of 16.

g. 45% of a number is 117.　　　　**h.** A number is 70% of 560.

i. A number is 30% of 120.　　　　**j.** 25% of a number is 21.

k. 61% of a number is 91.5.　　　　**l.** 60 is 48% of a number.

m. A number is 40% of 40.　　　　**n.** 5% of a number is 25.

o. 75% of a number is 84.　　　　**p.** 63% of a number is 56.7.

q. 56 is 25% of a number.　　　　**r.** A number is 4% of 75.

s. 48% of a number is 172.8.　　　　**t.** A number is 71% of 120.

u. 60% of a number is 18.　　　　**v.** 30% of a number is 45.

w. A number is 55% of 300.　　　　**x.** A number is 82% of 70.

9. A book costs $5.95. The tax on the book is 8% of the cost. What is the total cost of the book?

10. Jerry and Nadine had dinner at a Chinese restaurant. They left a 15% tip that was $2.70. How much did the meal cost before the tip?

11. An aerobics instructor maintains a strict diet of 2000 Calories per day. An 8 oz container of yogurt provides the instructor with 12% of her daily Calories. How many Calories does the yogurt provide?

12. In a school election, 285 students voted for Bill for the Student Council President. If 47.5% of the students voted for Bill, how many students voted in the election?

Study Guide
For use with Section 4

You Be the Critic   Percent

GOAL   **LEARN HOW TO:** • estimate and find percents
• find a missing part or whole

AS YOU: • analyze movie ratings
• find Audience Approval ratings
• find how many people rated a movie

Exploration 1: Estimating Percents

The symbol % stands for *percent*. **Percent** means "per hundred" or "out of 100." Four different ways to express a percent are shown at the right.

38%
38 Percent
38 per 100
38 out of 100

When solving problems involving percent, "nice" fractions can be used to help estimate solutions. "Nice" fractions are fractions that can be converted to percents easily. $\frac{1}{5}$, $\frac{1}{2}$, $\frac{3}{4}$, and $\frac{7}{10}$ are examples of "nice" fractions.

Example

Estimate the percent equivalent of 21 out of 40.

Sample Response

$\frac{21}{40}$ is slightly greater than the "nice" fraction $\frac{1}{2}$.

Since $\frac{1}{2} = 50\%$, $\frac{21}{40}$ is a little more than 50%.

Exploration 2: Finding Percents

You can find the percent equivalent for a ratio by using a proportion.

Example

Write the ratio $\frac{21}{40}$ as a percent.

Sample Response

$$\frac{21}{40} = \frac{x}{100}$$

$$40 \cdot x = 21 \cdot 100$$

$$40x = 2100$$

$$x = 52.5 \qquad \text{So, } \frac{21}{40} = 52.5\%.$$

Study Guide

For use with Section 4

Exploration 3: Finding Parts or Wholes

You can use proportions to find a missing part or whole.

■ Example

Set up and solve a proportion to find the number that is 35% of 70.

■ Sample Response ■

$$\begin{array}{cc} \text{Percent} & \text{Number} \end{array}$$

$$\begin{array}{c} \text{Part} \to \\ \text{Whole} \to \end{array} \frac{35}{100} = \frac{x}{70} \begin{array}{c} \leftarrow \text{Part} \\ \leftarrow \text{Whole} \end{array}$$

Now solve the proportion.

$$\frac{35}{100} = \frac{x}{70}$$

$$35 \cdot 70 = 100 \cdot x \quad \leftarrow \text{Use the cross products.}$$

$$2450 = 100x$$

$$\frac{2450}{100} = \frac{100x}{100} \quad \leftarrow \text{Divide both sides by 100.}$$

$$24.5 = x$$

So, 35% of 70 is 24.5.

■ Example

36 is 45% of some number. Use a proportion to find the number.

■ Sample Response ■

$$\begin{array}{cc} \text{Percent} & \text{Number} \end{array}$$

$$\begin{array}{c} \text{Part} \to \\ \text{Whole} \to \end{array} \frac{45}{100} = \frac{36}{y} \begin{array}{c} \leftarrow \text{Part} \\ \leftarrow \text{Whole} \end{array}$$

Now solve the proportion.

$$\frac{45}{100} = \frac{36}{y}$$

$$45 \cdot y = 100 \cdot 36 \quad \leftarrow \text{Use the cross products.}$$

$$45y = 3600$$

$$\frac{45y}{45} = \frac{3600}{45} \quad \leftarrow \text{Divide both sides by 45.}$$

$$y = 80$$

So, 36 is 45% of 80.

Name _____   Date _____

Study Guide: Practice & Application Exercises

For use with Section 4

Exploration 1

For Exercises 1–4, estimate the percent equivalent of each ratio.

1. $\frac{11}{23}$

2. $\frac{6}{21}$

3. $\frac{14}{17}$

4. $\frac{25}{26}$

5. A librarian estimated that 5 out every 13 library patrons ask the resource librarian a question. Estimate the percent of patrons who ask the resource librarian a question.

6. The owner of a bagel shop estimates that 19 out of every 25 customers order a plain bagel. Estimate the percent of customers who do *not* order a plain bagel.

Exploration 2

For Exercises 7–10, write each ratio as a percent. Round each answer to the nearest tenth.

7. $\frac{40}{60}$

8. $\frac{15}{25}$

9. $\frac{11}{50}$

10. $\frac{7}{9}$

11. In Marta's class, 8 out of 28 students got 100% on a science exam. What percent of the class did *not* get 100%?

12. Louie has $525 in his bank account. He spent $126 on new textbooks. What percent of the money in his bank account did Louie spend on textbooks?

Exploration 3

Find each unknown number.

13. 13% of a number is 84.5.

14. A number is 27% of 44.

15. A number is 40% of 120.

16. 98% of a number is 98.

17. 80% of a number is 20.

18. A number is 75% of 150.

19. A history test has 25 questions. How many questions must be answered correctly to score at least 80%?

20. On Friday, 26 of Ms. Gonzales' students wore jeans. If 65% of her students wore jeans, how many students are in Ms. Gonzales' class?

Math Thematics, Book 2
Teacher's Resource Book, Modules 5 and 6

Quick Quiz
For use after Section 4

1. Of 42 people surveyed, 27 rated a certain movie as 1 or 2 on a scale of 1 to 10. Use a "nice" fraction to estimate the percent of viewers giving this movie these "thumbs down" ratings.

2. Estimate the percent equivalent of $\frac{59}{81}$.

3. Write $\frac{42}{135}$ as a percent rounded to the nearest tenth.

4. 35% of what number is 63?

5. Suppose 75% of 6-year-olds weigh 50 lb or less. How many 6-year-olds would you expect to weigh 50 lb or less in a class of 32 age-six first-graders?

Name _____   Date _____

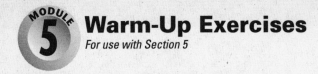

Warm-Up Exercises

Write the fraction as a decimal. Round answers to the nearest thousandth.

1. $\dfrac{3}{7}$

2. $\dfrac{11}{51}$

3. $\dfrac{67}{102}$

Choose the fraction that is closest to the percent given.

4. $50\% : \dfrac{15}{16}$ or $\dfrac{3}{7}$

5. $100\% : \dfrac{9}{8}$ or $\dfrac{12}{27}$

6. $25\% : \dfrac{13}{18}$ or $\dfrac{13}{60}$

ANSWERS

1. 0.429   2. 0.216   3. 0.657   4. $\dfrac{3}{7}$ 5. $\dfrac{9}{8}$ 6. $\dfrac{13}{80}$

Name _____ Date _____

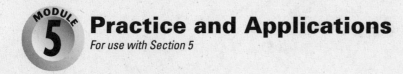

MODULE 5 **Practice and Applications**
For use with Section 5

For use with Exploration 1

1. Write each ratio as a fraction, a decimal, and a percent.

a. 2 : 3   **b.** 18 : 36   **c.** 12 : 20

d. 9 : 25   **e.** 3 : 9   **f.** 28 : 40

g. 27 : 36   **h.** 37 : 100   **i.** 9.5 : 10

2. Write each ratio, fraction, or decimal in percent form.

a. 7 : 50   **b.** $\frac{3}{4}$ **c.** 0.6

d. 38 : 50   **e.** $\frac{7}{8}$ **f.** 0.485

g. $\frac{30}{80}$ **h.** $\frac{4}{25}$ **i.** $\frac{45}{125}$

3. Use mental math to write each ratio as a percent.

a. $\frac{3}{20}$ **b.** $\frac{17}{25}$ **c.** $\frac{5}{20}$

d. $\frac{1}{9}$ **e.** $\frac{32}{100}$ **f.** $\frac{222}{333}$

g. $\frac{42}{84}$ **h.** $\frac{3.5}{50}$ **i.** $\frac{16}{32}$

For use with Exploration 2

4. To help the school dietician plan lunch menus, some students at a middle school took a survey of a random sample of their classmates to determine the top favorite lunch foods at their school. About 30% of the students surveyed chose pizza as their favorite lunch food. About 25% of the students surveyed chose sandwiches as their favorite lunch food. About 15% of the students surveyed chose pasta as their favorite lunch food. Suppose 600 students attend the school. How many of them would you expect to choose each food listed below?

a. pizza   **b.** sandwiches   **c.** pasta

5. About 79% of American households have a microwave oven. Estimate the number of households that have a microwave oven in a population of 600,000 people.

(continued)

Practice and Applications

For use with Section 5

For use with Exploration 3

6. Whitney's resting heart rate is 62 beats per minute. After 2 minutes of exercise, her heart rate is 93 beats per minute. Whitney's active heart rate is what percent of her resting heart rate?

7. Find each percent.

a. 15 is what percent of 60?

c. 44 is what percent of 80?

e. 45 is what percent of 50?

g. 114 is what percent of 120?

i. 209 is what percent of 209?

k. 13 is what percent of 10?

m. 38 is what percent of 20?

o. 12 is what percent of 80?

q. 30 is what percent of 24?

s. 165 is what percent of 100?

u. 35 is what percent of 25?

w. 120 is what percent of 75?

y. 180 is what percent of 80?

b. 27 is what percent of 90?

d. 48 is what percent of 64?

f. 68 is what percent of 85?

h. 25 is what percent of 125?

j. 28 is what percent of 80?

l. 51 is what percent of 60?

n. 154 is what percent of 140?

p. 18 is what percent of 40?

r. 125 is what percent of 50?

t. 70 is what percent of 35?

v. 78 is what percent of 65?

x. 7 is what percent of 4?

z. 69 is what percent of 46?

8. Tom's active heart rate is 180% of his resting heart rate. If his resting heart rate is 65 beats per minute, what is his active heart rate?

9. Carrie's resting heart rate is 70 beats per minute. She wants to increase her heart rate to 130% of her resting rate. What should her active heart rate be?

10. Tracy's active heart rate is 140% of her resting heart rate. If her resting heart rate is 70 beats per minute, what is her active heart rate?

Math Thematics, Book 2
Teacher's Resource Book, Modules 5 and 6

Name _____   Date _____

Study Guide

For use with Section 5

Make Every Shot Count   Percents and Predictions

GOAL **LEARN HOW TO:** • write a fraction as a decimal or percent
• estimate percents using "nice" fractions and mental math
• use percents to make predictions
• find percents greater than 100%

AS YOU: • test your free-throw ability
• examine basketball statistics
• compare your resting and active heart rates

Exploration 1: Fractions, Decimals, and Percents

Fraction-Decimal-Percent Equivalents

A ratio can be represented as a fraction, as a decimal, and as a percent.

> **Example**
>
> Write 24 out of 50 in ratio, fraction, decimal, and percent form.
>
> | Ratio form | Fraction form | Decimal form | Percent form |
> |---|---|---|---|
> | 24 to 50 or 24 : 50 | $\frac{24}{50}$ | 0.48 | 48% |

Exploration 2: Predicting Using Percents

Percents can be used to predict future outcomes.

> **Example**
>
> John has hit the bull's-eye of a target with a dart on 15 of 65 throws. How many bull's-eyes can he expect to get in his next 10 throws?
>
> **Sample Response**
>
> original fraction: $\frac{15}{65} = \frac{3}{13}$ → " nice" fraction: $\frac{3}{12} = \frac{1}{4}$
>
> So, $\frac{15}{65} \approx \frac{1}{4} = 25\%$.
>
> Since 25% of 10 = 0.25 • 10, or 2.5, John can expect to hit the bull's-eye 2 or 3 times in his next 10 throws.

Name _____   Date _____

Study Guide
For use with Section 5

Exploration 3: Percents Greater Than 100%

Some percent problems involve percents greater than 100%.

Example

36 is what percent of 15?

Sample Response

Think: 36 is greater than 15, so 36 is more than 100% of 15.

$$36 = \frac{x}{100} \cdot 15 \qquad \leftarrow x \text{ is the unknown part of 100\%.}$$

$$36 = \frac{15x}{100} \qquad \leftarrow \text{Simplify and solve for } x.$$

$$3600 = 15x$$

$$\frac{3600}{15} = \frac{15x}{15}$$

$$240 = x \qquad \text{So, 36 is 240\% of 15.}$$

Example

Sandra started a savings account with a deposit of $140. She now has $210 in the account. The current amount of money in Sandra's account is what percent of the original deposit?

Sample Response

Think: $210 is greater than $140, so $210 is more than 100% of $140.

$$210 = \frac{x}{100} \cdot 140 \qquad \leftarrow x \text{ is the unknown part of 100\%.}$$

$$210 = \frac{140x}{100} \qquad \leftarrow \text{Simplify and solve for } x.$$

$$21{,}000 = 140x$$

$$\frac{21{,}000}{140} = \frac{140x}{140}$$

$$150 = x \qquad \text{So, \$210 is 150\% of \$140.}$$

Name _____   Date _____

 Study Guide: Practice & Application Exercises
For use with Section 5

Exploration 1

For Exercises 1–8, write each ratio as a fraction, a decimal, and a percent.

1. 2 : 5   **2.** 12 : 36   **3.** 8 : 40   **4.** 18 : 100

5. 25 : 500   **6.** 5.4 : 21   **7.** 18 : 24   **8.** 25.8 : 200

Use mental math to write each ratio as a percent.

9. $\frac{11}{33}$ **10.** $\frac{8}{32}$ **11.** $\frac{24}{400}$ **12.** $\frac{16}{24}$

Exploration 2

13. About 30% of 66 students during the first lunch period chose pizza over hamburgers. If a school enrolls 580 students, how many can they expect to eat pizza?

14. Thelma has earned an A on 24% of all her math tests so far this year. There will be 20 more math tests this year. Estimate the number of A's she can expect to earn on these remaining tests.

15. Petra ran 23 out of 35 cross country races in less than 18 min. Based on these results, how many times in the next 15 races would you expect him to finish in less than 18 min?

Exploration 3

16. When Jeff begins typing, he types at a rate of 25 words per minute. After several minutes, his rate increases to 30 words per minute. What percent of Jeff's beginning speed is this rate of 30 words per minute?

Find each percent.

17. 18 is what percent of 45?   **18.** 46 is what percent of 80?

19. 278 is what percent of 139?   **20.** 81 is what percent of 60?

21. 201 is what percent of 201?   **22.** 315 is what percent of 63?

23. 84 is what percent of 70?   **24.** 231 is what percent of 110?

Name _____   Date _____

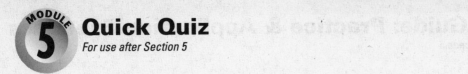
1. What is the batting average of a hitter who hit 62 times in 200 at-bats?

2. If a batter has hit 0.280 over the past three months, about how many hits would you expect her to get in her next 25 times at bat?

3. Write 10 : 85 in percent form rounded to the nearest tenth of a percent.

4. 84 is what percent of 60?

5. A 20-year-old's resting heart rate is 80 beats/min and his maximum heart rate is 200 beats/min. His maximum heart rate is what percent of his resting heart rate?

Name _____ Date _____

Practice and Applications

For use after Sections 1–5

For use with Section 1

1. Write each rate as a unit rate.

a. $\dfrac{46 \text{ min}}{5 \text{ mi}}$ b. $\dfrac{243 \text{ mi}}{9 \text{ gal}}$ c. $\dfrac{\$0.64}{8 \text{ min}}$

d. $\dfrac{176.4 \text{ km}}{6 \text{ L}}$ e. $\dfrac{38 \text{ min}}{4 \text{ mi}}$ f. $\dfrac{\$15}{4 \text{ lb}}$

g. $\dfrac{\$58.40}{4 \text{ hr}}$ h. $\dfrac{\$4.08}{6 \text{ bunches}}$ i. $\dfrac{45 \text{ min}}{6 \text{ mi}}$

2. To celebrate her fiftieth birthday, Beatrice ran a 50 mile race. Her time for the race was about 14 hr. Represent Beatrice's running pace as a unit rate. Round your answer to the nearest tenth.

3. Use the stem-and-leaf plot showing the spelling test scores for one class.

a. Do you notice any gaps or clusters in the data? Explain.

b. What is the range of the spelling test scores in the stem-and-leaf plot?

c. Find the median and mode of the data.

Spelling Test Scores

```
 6 | 9
 7 |
 8 | 0 0 2 5 6 7 8 8 9
 9 | 0 1 1 1 2 2 3 4 5 8
10 | 0
```

8 | 7 means 87

For use with Section 2

4. Make a frequency table for the data.
Scores on a ten-point quiz: 8, 6, 9, 9, 8, 8, 7, 10, 6, 8, 8, 6, 10, 7, 9

5. Alonso wants to know how effective the recycling program is in his neighborhood. Write 2 survey questions Alonso could ask his neighbors that would give him good information.

6. Use the histogram showing the age groups of children who attend swimming classes.

a. How many children who attend swimming classes are at least 9 years old?

b. Can you tell by looking at the histogram how many 6-year-old children take swimming lessons? Explain.

Children Enrolled in Swimming Classes

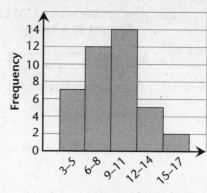

Age Groups

(continued)

Name _____   Date _____

For use with Section 3

7. Solve each proportion.

a. $\dfrac{m}{8} = \dfrac{4.2}{2.4}$ **b.** $\dfrac{24}{18} = \dfrac{38.4}{s}$ **c.** $\dfrac{6}{y} = \dfrac{21}{52.5}$

d. $\dfrac{14}{5} = \dfrac{70}{c}$ **e.** $\dfrac{a}{20} = \dfrac{24}{96}$ **f.** $\dfrac{9}{p} = \dfrac{45}{18}$

g. $\dfrac{5}{16} = \dfrac{17.5}{t}$ **h.** $\dfrac{16}{20} = \dfrac{4}{x}$ **i.** $\dfrac{36}{54} = \dfrac{v}{40.5}$

j. $\dfrac{c}{3} = \dfrac{24}{48}$ **k.** $\dfrac{33}{15} = \dfrac{w}{45}$ **l.** $\dfrac{7}{25} = \dfrac{1.4}{r}$

8. A dog eats about 12 lb of dog food every 15 days. How many pounds of dog food would you expect it to eat in 60 days?

9. Use the scatter plot to estimate the value of *y* when *x* is 12.

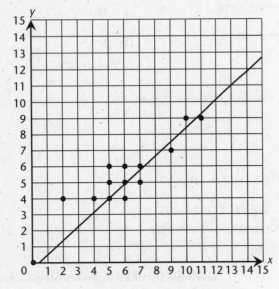

10.   **Lengths (in inches) of 20 Fish
Caught in a Lake**

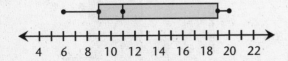

About how many of the fish measured less than 19 inches?

(continued)

Name _____   Date _____

 Practice and Applications
For use after Sections 1–5

For use with Section 4

11. Estimate the percent equivalent of each ratio.

　　a. $\frac{38}{79}$　　　　　　**b.** $\frac{1}{9}$　　　　　　**c.** $\frac{41}{52}$

　　d. $\frac{21}{80}$　　　　　　**e.** $\frac{63}{81}$　　　　　　**f.** $\frac{22}{50}$

12. Write each ratio as a percent. Round each answer to the nearest tenth.

　　a. $\frac{28}{60}$　　　　　　**b.** $\frac{17}{85}$　　　　　　**c.** $\frac{32}{128}$

　　d. $\frac{11}{20}$　　　　　　**e.** $\frac{23}{25}$　　　　　　**f.** $\frac{42}{78}$

13. Find each unknown number.

　　a. 25% of a number is 30.　　　　　　**b.** 105 is 75% of a number.

　　c. 60% of a number is 54.　　　　　　**d.** A number is 42% of 65.

　　e. A number is 36% of 150.　　　　　　**f.** A number is 15% of 60.

14. Members of a running club had lunch at the Whole Grain Burger
Palace. They left a 15% tip that totaled $9.30. How much did the
meal cost?

For use with Section 5

15. Use mental math to write each ratio as a percent.

　　a. $\frac{13}{20}$　　　　　　**b.** $\frac{22}{25}$　　　　　　**c.** $\frac{6}{24}$

16. About 76% of American households have a washing machine.
Estimate the number of American households that have a washing
machine in a population of 200,000 people.

17. Find each percent.

　　a. 135 is what percent of 100?　　　　　　**b.** 144 is what percent of 24?

　　c. 12 is what percent of 8?　　　　　　**d.** 237 is what percent of 237?

　　e. 168 is what percent of 96?　　　　　　**f.** 128 is what percent of 40?

MODULE 5   **REVIEW AND ASSESSMENT LABSHEET**

Bridge Length Graph (Use with Exercise 15 on page 389.)

Directions

- Plot the lengths of the bridges on the coordinate plane below.

- Draw a fitted line along the points on the graph.

Name of Bridge	Location	Length (ft)	Length (m)
Golden Gate	California, U.S.A.	4200	1280
Forth Road	Queensferry, Scotland	3300	1006
Longview	Washington, U.S.A.	1200	366
Howrah	Calcutta, India	1500	457
Sydney Harbor	Sydney, Australia	1670	509
Zdákov	Czech Republic	1244	380
Tatara	Ehime, Japan	2920	890
Dartford	Dartford, England	1476	450
Graf Spee	Germany	839	256
Amizade	Foz do Iguassu, Brazil	951	290
Skarnsudndet Bridge	Trondheim, Norway	1739	530
Fiumarella	Catanzaro, Italy	758	231

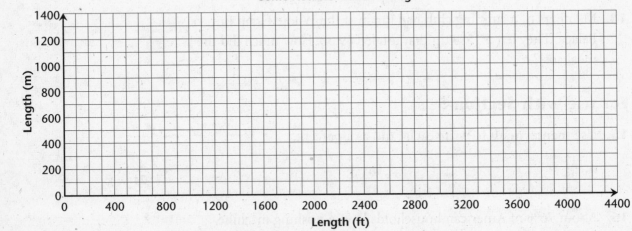

Some Notable Modern Bridges

a. About how many meters long is a 500-foot bridge?

b. About how many feet are in a meter?

Name _____ Date _____

Write each rate as a unit rate.

1. $\dfrac{420 \text{ km}}{5 \text{ hr}}$

2. $\dfrac{\$13.50}{3 \text{ lb}}$

Use the table for Questions 3 and 4. The table shows the number of community hospitals in ten different states.

3. Make a stem-and-leaf plot of the data. Be sure to include a key and a title.

Number of Hospitals in Selected States

State	Number of hospitals
Arizona	62
Colorado	70
Idaho	39
Maryland	50
Montana	54
New Mexico	37
North Dakota	40
South Carolina	62
Utah	43
West Virginia	57

4. Find the range, the median, and the mode for the numbers of hospitals.

range = _____ median = _____ mode = _____

Use the histogram for Questions 5 and 6.

5. How many triathletes finished the Ironman Triathlon in less than 11 hours?

6. Can you tell the slowest time in which anyone finished the triathlon? Explain.

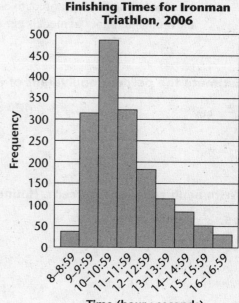

Finishing Times for Ironman Triathlon, 2006

Solve each proportion.

7. $\dfrac{15}{y} = \dfrac{60}{75}$

8. $\dfrac{z}{92} = \dfrac{24}{138}$

9. The fastest moving major glacier in the world is the Columbia Glacier in Alaska, which moves an average of 82 ft/day.

   a. How many days will it take for the glacier to move about 780 ft?

   b. How far will the glacier have moved in 2 weeks?

Name _____   Date _____

Test Form A
For use after Module 5

10. a. Use the data in the tables to make a scatter plot.

x	2	5	5	9	12	14	15
y	4	5	8	7	10	13	10

x	15	17	17	18	19
y	8	14	19	12	16

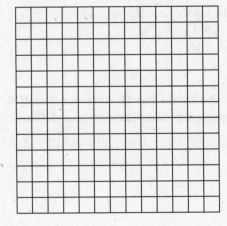

   b. Draw a fitted line for your scatter plot.

   c. Estimate the value of *y* when *x* is 8.

11.

**Number of Medals Won by the Top 20 Medal Winning
Countries at the 2004 Summer Olympics**

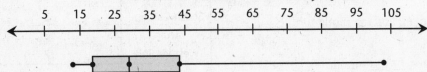

   a. Use the box-and-whisker plot to estimate the median number of medals per country.

   b. About how many countries won fewer than 43 medals?

Estimate the percent equivalent of each ratio.

12. $\frac{65}{99}$ **13.** $\frac{6}{29}$ **14.** $\frac{151}{203}$

Write each ratio as a percent. Round each answer to the nearest tenth.

15. $\frac{5}{13}$ **16.** $\frac{36}{41}$

Find each unknown number.

17. 38% of a number is 171.   **18.** A number is 92% of 150.   **19.** 465 is what percent of 240?

Name _____ Date _____

Test Form B
For use after Module 5

Write each rate as a unit rate.

1. $\dfrac{540 \text{ km}}{8 \text{ hr}}$

2. $\dfrac{\$18.20}{4 \text{ lb}}$

Use the table for Questions 3 and 4. The table shows the number of state legislators in ten selected states.

3. Make a stem-and-leaf plot of the data. Be sure to include a key and a title.

	Number of State Legislators for Selected States	
State	**Number of state legislators**
Arkansas	135
Connecticut	187
Hawaii	76
Kentucky	138
Michigan	148
Montana	150
New Mexico	112
Oklahoma	149
Tennessee	132
Wisconsin	132

4. Find the range, the median, and the mode for the numbers of state legislators.

   range = _____ median = _____ mode = _____

Use the histogram for Questions 5 and 6.

5. In how many years was the winning time for the Iditarod faster than 12 days?

6. Can you tell the course record for the Iditarod? Explain.

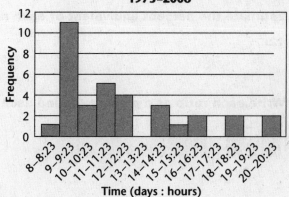

Winning Times for Iditarod Dog Sled Race, 1973–2006

Solve each proportion.

7. $\dfrac{6}{11} = \dfrac{30}{x}$

8. $\dfrac{z}{87} = \dfrac{15}{145}$

9. The fastest growing tree in the world grows at a rate of about 32.5 ft/yr.

   a. How many years would it take to grow 130 ft?

   b. About how many inches does it grow in 1 week?

Test Form B
For use after Module 5

10. a. Use the data in the tables to make a scatter plot.

x	2	3	4	8	8	11
y	16	12	14	11	15	11

x	11	13	14	15	16	18
y	13	10	8	12	11	8

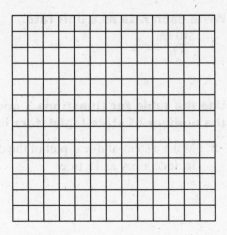

b. Draw a fitted line for your scatter plot.

c. Estimate the value of x when y is 8.

11. **Points per Game for a Basketball League's 12 Most Valuable Players**

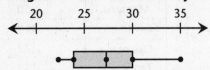

a. Use the box-and-whisker plot to estimate the median number of points per game.

b. About how many players scored fewer than 30 points per game?

Estimate the percent equivalent of each ratio.

12. $\frac{3}{29}$

13. $\frac{19}{61}$

14. $\frac{161}{182}$

Write each ratio as a percent. Round each answer to the nearest tenth.

15. $\frac{11}{12}$

16. $\frac{35}{62}$

Find each unknown number.

17. 68% of a number is 238.

18. A number is 36% of 650.

19. 250 is what percent of 160?

Name _____ Date _____

Standardized Test

For use after Module 5

1. Find the unit rate for 195.5 mi/8.5 gal.

   a. 25 mi/1 gal   **b.** 24 mi/1 gal

   c. 23 mi/1 gal   **d.** 22 mi/1 gal

2. Find the range of the data.

Spelling Test Scores

```
 5 | 9
 6 | 4 8
 7 | 2 5 5
 8 | 0 3 4 4 7 9
 9 | 0 0 2 8
10 | 0
```

5 | 9 represents a score of 59

   a. 39   **b.** 41

   c. 43   **d.** 44

3. If Christopher can type 65 words/min, how long will it take him to type a 3000-word essay?

   a. about 42 min   **b.** about 46 min

   c. about 50 min   **d.** about 54 min

4. Solve $\frac{4}{x} = \frac{30}{48}$.

   a. 2.5   **b.** 6.4

   c. 8.6   **d.** 360

5. Which of these is the best reason to use a scatter plot?

   a. to determine the relationship between two quantities and to make predictions

   b. to obtain the median of a set of data

   c. to determine the best way to organize the data

   d. to calculate the mean of a set of data

6. Which type of plot can be used to find the mode for a set of data?

   a. scatter plot

   b. histogram

   c. stem-and-leaf plot

   d. box-and-whisker plot

7. Estimate the percent equivalent of $\frac{142}{358}$.

   a. 20%   **b.** 33%

   c. 40%   **d.** 50%

8. What percent study more than 3 hr?

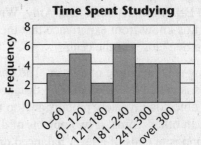

   a. about 14%   **b.** about 28%

   c. about 58%   **d.** about 64%

9. Which of the following fractions will give the largest result when written as a percent?

   a. $\frac{11}{14}$ **b.** $\frac{7}{9}$

   c. $\frac{8}{11}$ **d.** $\frac{5}{6}$

10. 323 is 38% of what number?

   a. 850   **b.** 436

   c. 249   **d.** 122.7

11. What is the median of the data shown in this box-and-whisker plot?

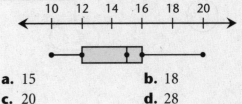

   a. 15   **b.** 18

   c. 20   **d.** 28

12. Find the frequency of two pets in this data about number of pets per household:

0, 4, 1, 3, 2, 0, 1, 13, 2, 4, 0, 1, 2, 5

   a. 2   **b.** 3

   c. 4   **d.** 5.5

Name _____   Date _____

A mobile is an intriguing way to display art or information. You can design a mobile if you understand proportions.

Each branch of a mobile is a carefully balanced lever, like a seesaw on the playground. Suppose Amy and Brian are sitting on opposite ends of a seesaw. It will not balance because Brian weighs more than Amy. What should they do? Many of us know from experience that the heavier person should move closer to the center.

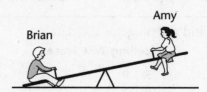

A seesaw is an example of a lever. The point on which it balances is called the fulcrum. The distance from the fulcrum to each object is inversely proportional to the weight of the objects. In other words, if two objects of different weights are on opposite ends of a lever balanced on a fulcrum, the heavier object will be closer to the fulcrum. So, for example, if Amy and Brian wish to balance on the seesaw, then the following must be true:

$$\frac{\text{Brian's weight}}{\text{Amy's weight}} = \frac{\text{Amy's distance from fulcrum}}{\text{Brian's distance from fulcrum}}$$

1. Ricky and Freddy are playing on a seesaw. Ricky weighs 75 pounds, and Freddy weighs 50 pounds. If Freddy sits 6 ft from the fulcrum, where should Ricky sit?

2. Look at the mobile shown below. Each set of weights must balance on its lever. Given the weights and distances shown, use proportions to find the unknown values.

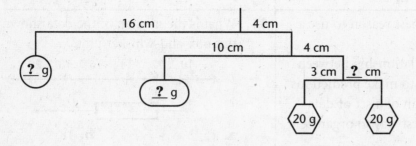

Contents

Book 2	Teacher's Resources for Module 6

Flights of Fancy

Name _____   Date _____

Module Diagnostic Test
For use before Module 6

1. Write and graph an inequality to represent the situation.   (Sec. 1)
   Currently the temperature is –5°F. The weather forecast predicts
   that throughout the day, the temperature will increase.

2. Which of the following is the area of the parallelogram in square feet?   (Sec. 1)

   A. $16 + 16 + 13 + 13$ **B.** $16 \cdot 12$ **C.** $16 \cdot 16$ **D.** $16 \cdot 13$

   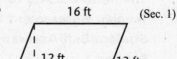

3. The lengths of the bases of a trapezoid are 12 in. and 8 in. If the area of   (Sec. 1)
   the trapezoid is 50 in.^{2}, what is the height of the trapezoid?

   A. 2.5 in.   **B.** 5 in.   **C.** 10 in.   **D.** 30 in.

4. If the theoretical probability of an event occurring is $\frac{2}{5}$, what is the   (Sec. 2)
   theoretical probability of the event *not* occurring?

   A. 0   **B.** $\frac{5}{2}$ **C.** $\frac{3}{5}$ **D.** $\frac{2}{5}$

5. A bag contains 6 marbles, 2 red, 3 white, and 1 blue. A marble is taken out   (Sec. 2)
   of the bag without looking. The color is recorded and the marble is returned
   to the bag. Then the process is repeated once more. What is the probability
   that two red marbles are drawn?

   A. $\frac{2}{3}$ **B.** $\frac{1}{3}$ **C.** $\frac{1}{6}$ **D.** $\frac{1}{9}$

**Find each of the following. If the principal square root is not a   (Sec. 3)
whole number, find the two consecutive integers it is between.**

6. $\sqrt{144}$ 7. $\sqrt{47}$

8. Sketch a net for the right triangular prism at the right.   (Sec. 3)
   Then find the surface area of the prism.

   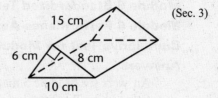

Module Diagnostic Test

For use before Module 6

9. Which of the following is the exact area of a circle with radius 5 in.?   (Sec. 3)

   A. 10π in.   **B.** 25π in.   **C.** 78.5 in.   **D.** 78.53981634 in.

10. Use the figure at the right to name the angles or pairs of angles   (Sec. 4)
    that fit each description. Lines j and k are parallel.

    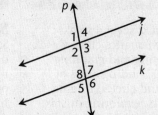

    a. two interior angles _____

    b. one pair of corresponding angles _____

    c. one pair of vertical angles _____

    d. one pair of alternate exterior angles _____

11. Find the sum of the measures of the interior angles in a convex hexagon.   (Sec. 4)

12. Two angles of a triangle each measure 70°. What is the measure of the   (Sec. 4)
    third angle?

    A. 40°   **B.** 70°   **C.** 120°   **D.** 140°

13. In $\triangle ABC$, the measure of $\angle A$ equals 75°. Which angle measure(s)   (Sec. 4)
    below are possible measures for $\angle B$ if triangle ABC is an obtuse triangle?

    A. 18°   **B.** 90°   **C.** 103°   **D.** 110°

14. $\triangle ABC$ is similar to $\triangle DEF$.   (Sec. 5)
    Find the values of x and y rounded to the nearest tenth. Show your work.

    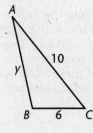   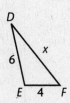

    A. $x = 8, y = 8$ **B.** $x = 7.2, y = 8$ **C.** $x = 9, y = 15$ **D.** $x = 6.7, y = 9$

The Math Gazette
Flights of Fancy

Sneak Preview!

Over the next several weeks in our mathematics class, we will be writing and graphing inequalities, finding areas of polygons and circles, finding square roots, exploring prisms, and exploring similarity while completing a thematic unit on flight. Some of the topics we will be discussing are:

▶ wing design

▶ parawings and other types of kites

▶ barnstorming pilots

▶ the first successful powered airplane flight

Ask Your Student

What are complementary events? (Sec. 2)

How can you find the surface area of a box? (Sec. 3)

Why did the Wright Flyer's wings have both vertical and diagonal struts? (Sec. 4)

What is a scale drawing? (Sec. 5)

Connections

Social Studies:
Students will learn about different aspects of flight. They may be interested in finding out more about the history of human aviation, both powered and not powered. Possible sources include encyclopedias and biographies of inventors.

Literature:
Students will read an excerpt from *Machines*, by Robert O'Brien. They may be interested in reading this book or others about the history of flight and pioneering pilots.

Science:
Students will learn how Bernoulli's Principle relates to the theme of the module. They will also calculate the wing loading of birds and investigate how such data was used in the design of early gliders.

E² Project

Following Section 3, students will have approximately one week to complete the Extended Exploration (E²), *Locating the Hub*. Students will decide how to locate the hub city for a small airline.

Students may use the following materials for the project:

▶ large sheets of blank paper for drawing diagrams

▶ rulers for measuring distances

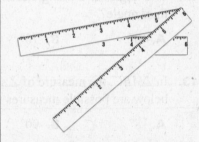

Module Project

After completing the module, students will test and analyze two designs for gliders. Then they will use geometry and measurement ideas to compare the designs and suggest ways to improve them.

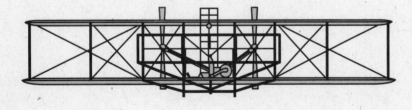

Flights of Fancy

Section Title	Mathematics Students Will Be Learning	Activities
1: Will It Fly?	◆ writing and graphing inequalities ◆ finding the areas of parallelograms, triangles, trapezoids, and composite shapes	◆ explore the effects of speed on air pressure ◆ compare the wing loading of birds and gliders ◆ model polygons with ice cream sticks
2: A Perfect Landing	◆ using areas of geometric figures to find theoretical probabilities ◆ finding theoretical probabilities for multistage experiments	◆ make an autogyro and use it to conduct probability experiments
3: Go Fly a Kite	◆ finding square roots ◆ identifying prisms and their parts ◆ using nets for 3-dimensional figures ◆ finding the surface areas of prisms ◆ finding the area of circles	◆ investigate kite designs ◆ make nets for prisms ◆ use the area of a parallelogram to approximate the area of a circle
4: Winging It!	◆ finding relationships among angles formed by parallel lines and a transversal ◆ finding the sum of the measures of the interior angles of a convex polygon	◆ make a model wing ◆ experiment with ways to make a wing rigid ◆ measure angles formed by parallel lines and a transversal
5: Barnstorming	◆ identifying similar and congruent polygons ◆ finding the scale of a scale drawing or model ◆ finding unknown measures in similar figures	◆ learn about the Curtiss Jenny airplane used by barnstormers ◆ compare scale drawings of a Curtiss Jenny

Activities to do at Home

- Find the area of a circular household object, such as a compact disc, the top of a can, or a wheel. (After Sec. 3)

- Sketch a net for a cereal box. Measure the length, width, and height of the box and use the measurements to label the dimensions of the net. Then use the net to find the surface area of the box. (After Sec. 3)

- Make a scale drawing of your home or neighborhood. Include a scale and explain how you chose it. (After Sec. 5)

Related Topics

You may want to discuss these related topics with your student:

 Industrial design

 Mechanical drafting

 Probability

Name _____   Problem _____

☆ *The star indicates that you excelled in some way.*

 Problem Solving

❶   ❷   ❸   ❹   ❺ ☆→

You did not understand the problem well enough to get started or you did not show any work.

You understood the problem well enough to make a plan and to work toward a solution.

You made a plan, you used it to solve the problem, and you verified your solution.

 Mathematical Language

❶   ❷   ❸   ❹   ❺ ☆→

You did not use any mathematical vocabulary or symbols, or you did not use them correctly, or your use was not appropriate.

You used appropriate mathematical language, but the way it was used was not always correct or other terms and symbols were needed.

You used mathematical language that was correct and appropriate to make your meaning clear.

 Representations

❶   ❷   ❸   ❹   ❺ ☆→

You did not use any representations such as equations, tables, graphs, or diagrams to help solve the problem or explain your solution.

You made appropriate representations to help solve the problem or help you explain your solution, but they were not always correct or other representations were needed.

You used appropriate and correct representations to solve the problem or explain your solution.

 Connections

❶   ❷   ❸   ❹   ❺ ☆→

You attempted or solved the problem and then stopped.

You found patterns and used them to extend the solution to other cases, or you recognized that this problem relates to other problems, mathematical ideas, or applications.

You extended the ideas in the solution to the general case, or you showed how this problem relates to other problems, mathematical ideas, or applications.

 Presentation

❶   ❷   ❸   ❹   ❺ ☆→

The presentation of your solution and reasoning is unclear to others.

The presentation of your solution and reasoning is clear in most places, but others may have trouble understanding parts of it.

The presentation of your solution and reasoning is clear and can be understood by others.

Content Used: _____   **Computational Errors:**   Yes ☐   No ☐

Notes on Errors: _____

_____

Name _____   Problem _____

Student Self-Assessment Scales

For use with Module 6

▬▬ If your score is in the shaded area, explain why on the back of this sheet and stop.

☆ The star indicates that you excelled in some way.

 Problem Solving

①②③④⑤ →☆→

① I did not understand the problem well enough to get started or I did not show any work.

③ I understood the problem well enough to make a plan and to work toward a solution.

⑤ I made a plan, I used it to solve the problem, and I verified my solution.

 Mathematical Language

①②③④⑤ →☆→

① I did not use any mathematical vocabulary or symbols, or I did not use them correctly, or my use was not appropriate.

③ I used appropriate mathematical language, but the way it was used was not always correct or other terms and symbols were needed.

⑤ I used mathematical language that was correct and appropriate to make my meaning clear.

 Representations

①②③④⑤ →☆→

① I did not use any representations such as equations, tables, graphs, or diagrams to help solve the problem or explain my solution.

③ I made appropriate representations to help solve the problem or help me explain my solution, but they were not always correct or other representations were needed.

⑤ I used appropriate and correct representations to solve the problem or explain my solution.

 Connections

①②③④⑤ →☆→

① I attempted or solved the problem and then stopped.

③ I found patterns and used them to extend the solution to other cases, or I recognized that this problem relates to other problems, mathematical ideas, or applications.

⑤ I extended the ideas in the solution to the general case, or I showed how this problem relates to other problems, mathematical ideas, or applications.

 Presentation

①②③④⑤ →☆→

① The presentation of my solution and reasoning is unclear to others.

③ The presentation of my solution and reasoning is clear in most places, but others may have trouble understanding parts of it.

⑤ The presentation of my solution and reasoning is clear and can be understood by others.

Warm-Up Exercises

For use with Section 1

Write each inequality in words.

1. $2s > 8$

2. $b \leq 14$

State the formula for finding the area of each figure.

3. a square

4. a rectangle

Multiply.

5. $\frac{1}{2}(8 + 22)$

6. $\left(\frac{15}{3}\right)7$

ANSWERS

1. Two times s is greater than 8.   2. b is less than or equal to 14.   3. $a = s^2$, where s is the length of the side of the square.   4. $A = lw$, where l is the length and w is the width of the rectangle.
5. 15   6. 35

Trapezoids (Use with Question 19 on page 399.)

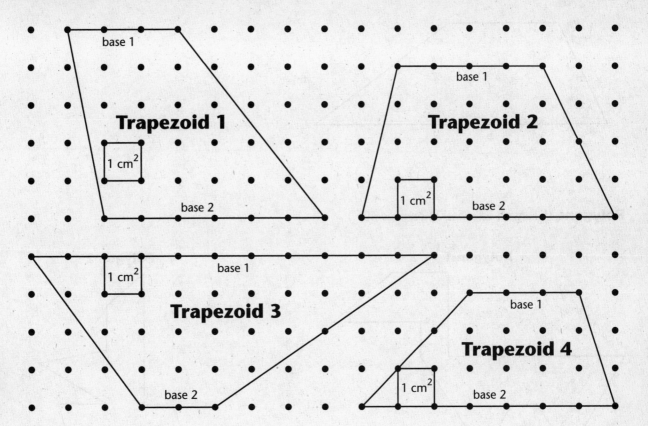

Trapezoids (Use with Exercise 23 on page 404.)

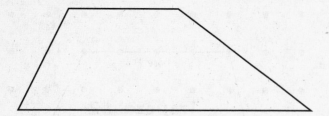

Polygons (Use with Exercise 24 on page 405.)

Polygon 1

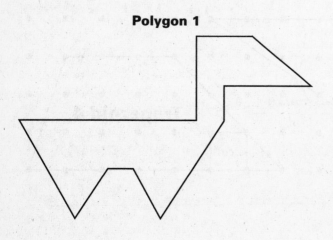

Polygon 2

Math Thematics, Book 2
Teacher's Resource Book, Modules 5 and 6

Practice and Applications

For use with Section 1

For use with Exploration 1

1. Write an inequality to represent each statement. Then graph the inequality on a number line.

   a. x is less than 5.

   b. b is greater than or equal to 7.

   c. h is greater than 6 and less than or equal to 14.

   d. 2 is less than p, and p is less than 9.

   e. a is greater than 3.

   f. k is less than or equal to 6.

   g. r is greater than 2 and less than 5.

   h. s is greater than 4 and less than 17.

   i. 4 is less than t, and t is less than or equal to 16.

   j. b is greater than 8 and less than or equal to 10.

2. Use the graph below.

   Lengths of North American Owls (in inches)

   a. One of the smallest owls in North America is the elf owl. Estimate its length.

   b. Estimate the range of sizes of the owls represented in the graph.

For use with Exploration 2

3. Tell whether each quadrilateral is a parallelogram. If a quadrilateral is not a parallelogram, explain why not.

   a.

   b.

   c.

4. Classify each polygon as *concave* or *convex*.

   a.

   b.

   c.

5. Draw two 6-sided polygons, one that is convex and one that is concave.

(continued)

Name _____ Date _____

For use with Exploration 3

6. Find the area of the trapezoid with the given measurements.

  a. $b_1 = 6$ in., $b_2 = 2$ in., $h = 5$ in.

  b. $b_1 = 9$ m, $b_2 = 6$ m, $h = 3$ m

  c. $b_1 = 4.3$ m, $b_2 = 6.1$ m, $h = 3.8$ m

  d. $b_1 = 3\frac{3}{4}$ in., $b_2 = 2\frac{1}{4}$ in., $h = 5\frac{1}{2}$ in.

  e. $b_1 = 2.35$ cm, $b_2 = 4.4$ cm, $h = 5.2$ cm

7. Find the area of each trapezoid.

  a.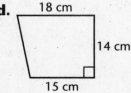

  b.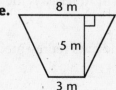

  c.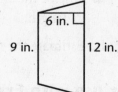

  d.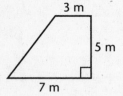

  e.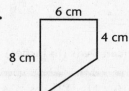

  f.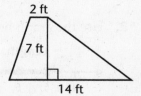

8. For each trapezoid, find the unknown dimension or the area.

  a.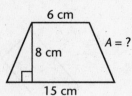

  b.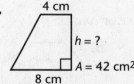

  c.

  d.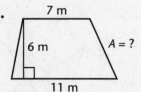

  e.

  f.

9. Mr. Carlisle is building a deck. The floor of the deck is in the shape of a trapezoid. How many square feet of lumber will Mr. Carlisle need if the dimensions of the deck are $b_1 = 12$ ft, $b_2 = 18$ ft, and $h = 15$ ft?

Name _____ Date _____

Study Guide
For use with Section 1

Will It Fly?   Inequalities and Polygons

GOAL   **LEARN HOW TO:** • write and graph inequalities
• find the areas of polygons
• find the area of a trapezoid

AS YOU: • investigate how wing design makes flight possible
• study the wing of an albatross
• examine the wing design of gliders

Exploration 1: Inequalities

A mathematical sentence that contains one or more of the symbols
$>$, $<$, $\geq$, or $\leq$ is an **inequality**.

Example

Write an inequality to represent each statement. Then graph the inequality.

a. y is less than 5.

b. 3 is less than or equal to x, and x is less than or equal to 6.

Sample Response

a. $y < 5$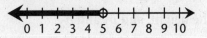
                0 1 2 3 4 5 6 7 8 9 10

The open circle means 5 is not included.

b. $3 \leq x \leq 6$ ←|+|+|●+|+|●|+|+|→
                        0 1 2 3 4 5 6 7 8 9 10

The solid circles mean 3 and 6 are included.

Exploration 2: Areas of Polygons

Polygons

A **polygon** is a simple, closed, flat figure made of segments.
A polygon can be either **convex** or **concave**. If a polygon is
convex, every line that contains two of its vertices passes
through the interior of the polygon. For a concave polygon,
there is at least one line containing two vertices that does not
pass through the interior of the polygon. In a **regular polygon**,
all the segments are the same length, and all the angles are
equal in measure.

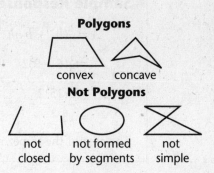

Polygons

convex   concave

Not Polygons

not   not formed   not
closed   by segments   simple

Name _____ Date _____

Study Guide
For use with Section 1

A polygon that has *four sides* is a **quadrilateral**.
A **parallelogram** is a quadrilateral that has *two pairs of parallel sides*.

The area of a parallelogram is the product of the length of its base and its height. The area of a triangle is half the length of its base times its height.

You can find the area of some polygons by separating them into triangles and parallelograms.

Quadrilateral   **Parallelogram**

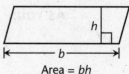

Parallelogram

Area = bh

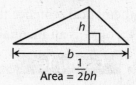

Triangle

Area = $\frac{1}{2}bh$

Exploration 3: Trapezoids

A **trapezoid** is a *quadrilateral* that has exactly *one pair of parallel sides*. The sides that are parallel are the *bases* of the trapezoid, b_1 and b_2. The *height* of the trapezoid is the distance between its two bases.

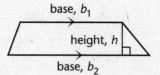

base, b_1

height, h

base, b_2

The area of a trapezoid can be calculated using the formula $A = \frac{1}{2}(b_1 + b_2)h$, where A is the area, h is the height, and b_1 and b_2 are the lengths of the two bases.

Example

Find the area of the trapezoid shown.

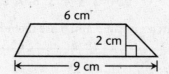

6 cm

2 cm

9 cm

■ **Sample Response** ■

$A = \frac{1}{2}(b_1 + b_2)h$

$\quad = \frac{1}{2}(6 + 9)2 \quad \leftarrow$ Substitute 6 for b_1, 9 for b_2, and 2 for h.

$\quad = \frac{1}{2}(15)2$

$\quad = 15$

The area of the trapezoid is 15 cm^2.

Math Thematics, Book 2
Teacher's Resource Book, Modules 5 and 6

6-14

Name _____   Date _____

Exploration 1

For Exercises 1–4, write an inequality to represent each statement. Then graph the inequality on a number line.

1. *w* is greater than 5.

2. *j* is less than or equal to 13.

3. 1 is less than *y*, and *y* is less than 4.

4. *r* is greater than 3 and less than or equal to 7.

5. a. Write an inequality to represent the possible wingspans of California condors and an inequality to represent the possible body lengths of California condors.

California Condors

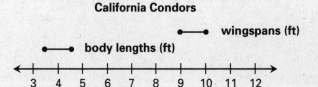

b. Is it possible for the body length of one condor to be greater than the wingspan of another condor? Explain.

Exploration 2

Tell whether each quadrilateral is a parallelogram. If a quadrilateral is not a parallelogram, explain why not.

6.

7.
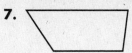

Classify each polygon as *convex* or *concave*.

8.
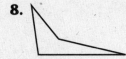

9.

Exploration 3

Find the area of each trapezoid.

10.
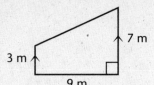

11.
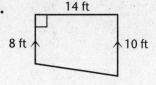

12.

Find each unknown dimension.

13. trapezoid: $h = 15$ m, $b_1 = 8$ m, $A = 135$ m², $b_2 =$ ___?___

14. trapezoid: $b_1 = 17$ ft, $b_2 = 21$ ft, $A = 57$ ft², $h =$ ___?___

Name _____   Date _____

1. Write and graph an inequality to represent this statement:

   x is less than or equal to 18 and greater than 15.

2. Alyssa always spends at least 25 min a day practicing the tuba. Write
an inequality to show how many minutes she practices in a week.

3. Identify the polygon at the right as *convex* or *concave*.
Tell how you know.

4. Describe two ways to find the area of the trapezoid
at the right.

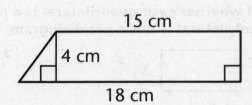

5. What is the area of the trapezoid?

Name _____ Date _____

Find each probability.

1. rolling a 2 on a 6-sided number cube

2. rolling an even number on a 6-sided number cube

3. picking an even number from the numbers 0–9

4. selecting a red pen if there are 2 red pens, 2 blue pens, and 1 black pen in a container

ANSWERS

1. $\frac{1}{6}$ 2. $\frac{1}{2}$ 3. $\frac{1}{2}$ 4. $\frac{2}{5}$

Name _____ Date _____

For use with Exploration 1

1. Find the probability that a small object dropped on each figure will land on the shaded target.

a.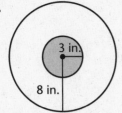

b.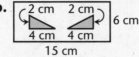

c.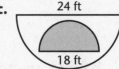

d.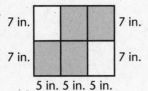

e.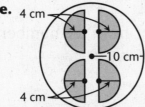

f.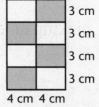

2. Suppose the probability that an object dropped onto the square shown at the right will land inside the shaded star is $\frac{3}{4}$.

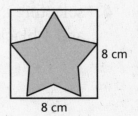

a. What is the probability that the object will land in the unshaded area?

b. What is the area of the star?

3. A small object is tossed onto a game board. If the object lands on the shaded area, Player I wins. If not, Player II wins.

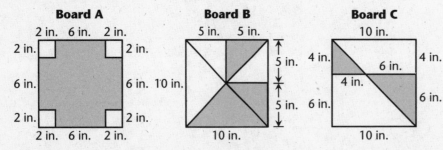

a. Which game board is fair to both players, that is, makes their chances of winning equal?

b. If you want Player I to have a greater chance of winning, which game board should you choose?

(continued)

Name _____ Date _____

Practice and Applications
For use with Section 2

For use with Exploration 2

4. Consider the experiment of flipping a coin and rolling a 6-sided number cube. Shade a grid to find the probability of each event.

   a. heads and the number 3   **b.** tails and a number less than 4

   c. tails and an even number   **d.** heads and a number greater than 1

   e. heads and a 5 or 6   **f.** tails and a number less than 5

5. A bag contains 1 green marble and 3 yellow marbles. Three marbles are removed from the bag one after another. After each marble is removed, its color is recorded and the marble is put back into the bag before the next marble is removed.

Copy and complete the tree diagram at the right to show the outcomes of this experiment. Label each branch of the tree with the probability.

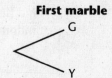

6. Use the tree diagram from Exercise 5 to find the probability of each event. Round answers to the nearest tenth of a percent.

   a. drawing three green marbles   **b.** drawing three yellow marbles

   c. drawing a green, a yellow,   **d.** drawing a yellow, a yellow,
       and a green marble   and a green marble

   e. drawing exactly two yellow marbles   **f.** drawing exactly two green marbles

   g. drawing at least one yellow marble   **h.** drawing at least one green marble

7. Suppose the probability that it will snow in Yellowstone this week is $\frac{3}{8}$ each day.

   a. What is the probability that it will not snow on a given day?

   b. Make a tree diagram to find all the possible outcomes for two consecutive days.

   c. Use a grid to find the probability of snow on two consecutive days.

   d. What is the probability that it will not snow on two consecutive days?

   e. What is the probability it will snow the first day and *not* snow the second day?

Name _____   Date _____

Study Guide
For use with Section 2

A Perfect Landing   Probability

GOAL   **LEARN HOW TO:** • use areas to find theoretical probabilities
• find the probabilities of complementary events
• find theoretical probabilities for a multistage experiment

AS YOU: • examine the results of a skydiving simulation
• simulate repeated parachute jumps

Exploration 1: Geometric Probability

A probability that is based on lengths, areas, or volumes of figures is a
geometric probability.

Example

Find the probability that a point selected at
random on $\overline{PR}$ is on $\overline{QR}$.

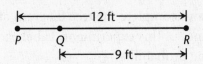

Sample Response

The probability that a point which is on $\overline{PR}$ is located on $\overline{QR}$ is:

$$\frac{\text{length of } \overline{QR}}{\text{length of } \overline{PR}} = \frac{9}{12} = \frac{3}{4}, \text{ or } 75\%.$$

Two events are **complementary events** if one or the other must occur, but
they cannot both happen at the same time. The sum of the probabilities of
two complementary events is 1.

Example

The events *rolling an even number* and *rolling an odd number* when a number cube is
rolled are complementary events.

The events *landing heads* and *landing tails* when a coin is flipped are complementary
events.

When selecting a card at random from a standard deck of cards, the events *drawing a
red card* and *drawing a black card* are complementary events.

Study Guide

For use with Section 2

Exploration 2: Multistage Experiments

A **tree diagram** is a display whose branches show all the possible outcomes of an experiment. To find the probability of a particular outcome using a tree diagram, find the product of the probabilities along the path leading to that outcome.

A **multistage experiment** consists of doing two or more events one after the other. You can find the probability of the outcomes of a multistage experiment by shading a grid or constructing a tree diagram.

Example

A spinner has three equal sectors numbered 1–3. If the spinner is spun twice, what is the probability that a 3 is spun both times?

Sample Response

There is a 1 in 3 chance of spinning a 3 on any spin.

Method 1: Use a 3×3 grid.

Start on the left and shade $\frac{1}{3}$ of the columns (1 column) to show the probability that a 3 is spun on the first spin.

Start at the top and shade $\frac{1}{3}$ of the rows (1 row) to show the probability that the second spin is a 3.

The probability that the first and the second spins will both be a 3 is represented by the region of the grid that was shaded twice. So, the probability is $\frac{1}{9}$.

Method 2: Use a tree diagram.

From the diagram, $P(3, 3) = \frac{1}{3} \cdot \frac{1}{3} = \frac{1}{9}$.

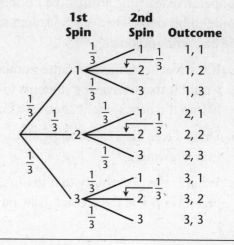

Name _____   Date _____

Study Guide: Practice & Application Exercises

MODULE 6

For use with Section 2

Exploration 1

1. Suppose a point on $\overline{XZ}$ is selected at random.
Find the probability that the point is on $\overline{XY}$.

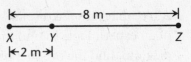

2. Find the probability that a small object dropped on
the parallelogram will land on the shaded region.

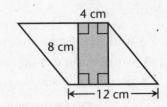

Exploration 2

3. A bag contains 4 green chips and 5 red chips. Two chips are removed
from the bag one after another. After each chip is removed, its color is
recorded and the chip is put back into the bag before the next chip is
removed.

  a. Draw a 9 × 9 grid. Shade it to find the probability of drawing a
  green chip on the first pick and a red chip on the second pick.

  b. Draw a tree diagram to show the possible outcomes of this
  experiment. Label each branch of the diagram with the
  probability of the outcome represented by it.

  c. Use the tree diagram from part (b) to find the probability of
  drawing 2 red chips.

4. A teacher uses a bag containing 4 cubes—one red, one green,
one yellow, and one black—to assign his 24 students to one of four
cooperative learning groups. To do this, he has groups of 4 students
come to his desk, where each student selects one of the cubes from
the bag without looking.

  a. If the teacher wants the same number of students in each group,
  would it make sense for students to put their cube back in the bag
  before the next student chooses a cube? Why or why not?

  b. Draw a tree diagram to show all the possible outcomes for a set of
  four drawings.

  c. What is the probability that the first draw puts a student on the
  green team and the second draw puts a student on the red team?

Math Thematics, Book 2
Teacher's Resource Book, Modules 5 and 6

6-22

Name _____ Date _____

1. A dart is equally likely to land in any region of the parallelogram below. Find the theoretical probability that a dart thrown at the target

    a. will land in the shaded triangle.

    b. will *not* land in the shaded triangle.

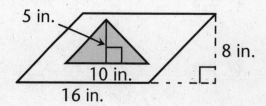

2. Consider the experiment of spinning the two spinners shown and recording the two colors. Find the probability of getting two reds.

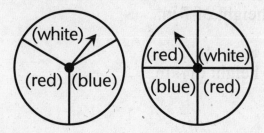

3. Use a tree diagram to show the probability of getting red and blue in either order with the two spinners above.

Math Thematics, Book 2
Teacher's Resource Book, Modules 5 and 6   **6-23**

Name _____   Date _____

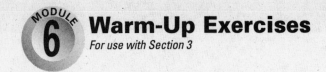
Warm-Up Exercises
For use with Section 3

Find each value when *m* = 4.

1. m^2

2. $3m^3$

Find the area of each figure.

3. a triangle with a base of 16 in. and a height of 7 in.

4. a rectangle with a base of 13 m and a height of 4 m

5. a square with side lengths of 2.5 cm

ANSWERS

1. 16   2. 192   3. 56 in.^{2} 4. 52 m^2 5. 6.25 cm^2

MODULE 6   **LABSHEET** **3A**

Circle (Use with Question 22 on page 426.)

Directions

a. Cut out the circle.

b. Cut apart the eight sectors and arrange them to form the figure shown below.

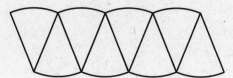

c. Tape the figure to a sheet of paper.

Cut out the circle and then cut along the solid line segments.

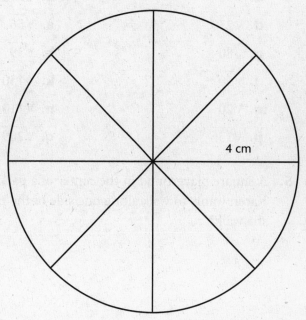

4 cm

Name _____ Date _____

Practice and Applications
For use with Section 3

For use with Exploration 1

1. Show that each number is a perfect square.

   a. 49   **b.** 900   **c.** 225

2. Find each square root.

   a. $\sqrt{144}$ **b.** $\sqrt{36}$ **c.** $\sqrt{0}$

   d. $\sqrt{169}$ **e.** $-\sqrt{16}$ **f.** $-\sqrt{100}$

   g. $\sqrt{400}$ **h.** $-\sqrt{121}$ **i.** $-\sqrt{81}$

    j. $-\sqrt{196}$ **k.** $\sqrt{324}$ **l.** $-\sqrt{256}$

   m. $\sqrt{289}$ **n.** $-\sqrt{25}$ **o.** $-\sqrt{1}$

   p. $\sqrt{64}$ **q.** $-\sqrt{0}$ **r.** $\sqrt{361}$

3. Give two consecutive whole numbers that each principal square root lies between. Then estimate each square root to the nearest tenth.

   a. $\sqrt{18}$ **b.** $\sqrt{46}$ **c.** $\sqrt{115}$

   d. $\sqrt{30}$ **e.** $\sqrt{7}$ **f.** $\sqrt{140}$

4. Estimate each square root to the nearest tenth.

   a. $\sqrt{72}$ **b.** $\sqrt{160}$ **c.** $\sqrt{28}$

   d. $\sqrt{230}$ **e.** $\sqrt{56}$ **f.** $\sqrt{415}$

   g. $\sqrt{80}$ **h.** $\sqrt{39}$ **i.** $\sqrt{249}$

    j. $\sqrt{50}$ **k.** $\sqrt{130}$ **l.** $\sqrt{260}$

   m. $\sqrt{20}$ **n.** $\sqrt{110}$ **o.** $\sqrt{61}$

   p. $\sqrt{136}$ **q.** $\sqrt{209}$ **r.** $\sqrt{42}$

5. A square playground in the center of a park has an area of 784 ft^2. Karen wants to walk along one side of the playground. How far does she walk?

(continued)

Name _____ Date _____

Practice and Applications

For use with Section 3

For use with Exploration 2

6. Use the prism shown.

    a. What kind of prism is this?

    b. How many faces, vertices, and edges does this prism have?

7. Use the prism shown.

    a. What kind of prism is this?

    b. How many faces, vertices, and edges does this prism have?

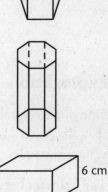

8. Use the right rectangular prism shown.

    a. Sketch a net for the prism.

    b. Find the surface area of the prism.

9. A box of macaroni and cheese is 7 in. tall, 4 in. long, and 2 in. wide. What is the surface area of the box?

For use with Exploration 3

10. Use π to write an expression for the exact area of each circle. Then use 3.14 or the ⬚π key on a calculator to find the approximate area. Round your answer to the nearest hundredth.

a.

b.

c.

d.

e.

f.

11. A circular window has a diameter of 18 in. What is the area of the window?

Name _____ Date _____

Study Guide
For use with Section 3

Go Fly a Kite!   Square Roots, Surface Area, and Area of a Circle

GOAL **LEARN HOW TO:** • find square roots of perfect squares
• estimate square roots to the nearest tenth
• identify prisms and their parts
• draw a net for a prism
• find the surface area of a prism
• find the area of a circle

AS YOU: • investigate parawing, box kite, and kite designs

Exploration 1: Square Roots

One of two equal factors of a number is a **square root** of that number.
If $A = s^2$, then s is a square root of A. Every positive number has two
square roots. For example, the square roots of 400 are 20 and –20.

The **principal square root** of a *positive* number, indicated by $\sqrt{}$, is the
positive square root. A number is a **perfect square** if its principal square
root is a whole number.

> ### Example
>
> **a.** $\sqrt{625} = 25$, so 625 is a perfect square, and 25 is the principal square root of 625.
>
> **b.** $\sqrt{114} \approx 10.58$, so 114 is not a perfect square. The approximation 10.58 is the
> principal square root of 114.

Exploration 2: Surface Areas of Prisms

Prisms and Surface Area

A **polyhedron** is a 3-dimensional object made up of flat surfaces, or **faces,**
shaped like polygons. A **prism** is a polyhedron in which two of the faces,
the **bases,** are parallel and congruent. The other faces are parallelograms.
Pairs of faces meet in segments called **edges,** and the edges meet in points
called **vertices.** In a **right prism,** the non-base faces are rectangles, and the
bases are aligned vertically. In an **oblique prism,** the non-base faces are
not rectangular and do not align vertically.

The prism shown is a right prism because its non-base
faces are rectangular.

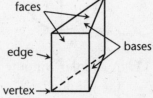

Name _____ Date _____

Study Guide
For use with Section 3

The **surface area** of a prism is the sum of the areas of all its faces.
You can use a **net,** or flat pattern, to help find the surface area of a prism.

Example

a. Name the prism at the right. Tell how many faces,
how many vertices, and how many edges it has.

b. Draw a net for the prism and use it to find the surface area.

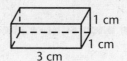

Sample Response

a. This is a right rectangular prism. It has 6 faces, 8 vertices, and 12 edges.

b.

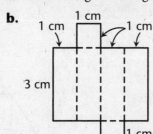

Each square has an area of 1 cm².
Each rectangle has an area of 3 cm².
1 + 1 + 3 + 3 +3 +3 = 14

The surface area of the prism is 14 cm².

Exploration 3: Area of a Circle

The area, A, of a circle is equal to πr^2, where r is the radius of the circle.
Recall that the radius of a circle is half its diameter and that π is a
constant approximated by 3.14.

Example

Find the area of a circle with diameter 2.4 cm.

Sample Response

Since the diameter of the circle is 2.4 cm, the radius is $\frac{1}{2}(2.4)$, or 1.2 cm.

$$A = \pi r^2$$
$$= \pi(1.2)^2$$
$$= 1.44\pi$$

The exact area of the circle is 1.44π cm².

To find a numerical approximation for the area, substitute 3.14 for π or use the π key.

$$A \approx 3.14 \cdot 1.44 = 4.5216$$

An approximate area of the circle is 4.52 cm².

Name _____   Date _____

Exploration 1

Find each square root. If the square root is not a whole number, find the two consecutive integers it is between.

1. $\sqrt{121}$ **2.** $\sqrt{81}$ **3.** $-\sqrt{36}$ **4.** $\sqrt{150}$

Estimate each square root to the nearest tenth.

5. $\sqrt{7}$ **6.** $\sqrt{43}$ **7.** $\sqrt{20}$ **8.** $\sqrt{155}$

9. Arturo and his family are moving to a new house. Both Arturo's old and new bedrooms are square. The area of Arturo's old bedroom was 100 ft^2. The area of Arturo's new bedroom is 120 ft^2. By how many feet did each side of Arturo's bedroom increase? Round your answer to the nearest hundredth.

Exploration 2

For Exercises 10 and 11, use the prism shown at the right.

10. What kind of prism is this?

11. How many faces, vertices, and edges does this prism have?

12. Use the right rectangular prism shown.

    a. Sketch a net for the prism.

    b. Find the area of each face.

    c. Find the surface area of the prism.

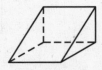

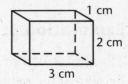

1 cm
2 cm
3 cm

Exploration 3

Use π to write an expression for the exact area of each circle. Then use 3.14 or the π key on a calculator to find the approximate area. Round your answer to the nearest hundredth.

13. radius: 4 mm   **14.** diameter: 5.4 ft   **15.** radius: 3.1 cm

Find the approximate radius of a circle with each area. Use 3.14 for π.

16. $A = 78$ yd^2 **17.** $A = 32$ ft^2 **18.** $A = 108$ cm^2

Math Thematics, Book 2
Teacher's Resource Book, Modules 5 and 6

Name _____   Date _____

1. Find $\sqrt{400}$.

2. Between what two consecutive whole numbers does $\sqrt{22}$ lie?

3. a. What is the name of this prism?

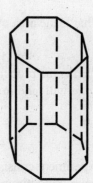

    b. How many faces, edges, and vertices does it have?

4. What is the surface area of a right rectangular prism with base 10 cm by 12 cm and height 20 cm?

5. Use π to write an expression for the exact area of a circle with diameter 2.4 in. Then use 3.14 or the π key on your calculator to find the approximate area. Round to the nearest hundredth.

Name _____   Date _____

1. George has at least $240 but no more than $275 in his checking account. Write and graph an inequality to represent this situation.

For Question 2, refer to the figure at the right.

2. **a.** What is the area of parallelogram *ABCD*?

   b. What is the area of triangle *BEC*?

   c. What is the probability that a dart thrown at the figure will land in the triangle?

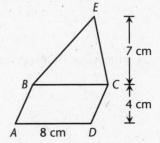

3. An experiment consists of spinning Spinner 1 and then spinning Spinner 2.

   a. Draw a tree diagram showing all of the possible outcomes of this experiment.

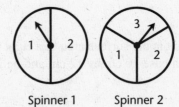

Spinner 1   Spinner 2

   b. What is the theoretical probability of spinning two even numbers?

   c. What is the theoretical probability of spinning at least one 2?

4. A trapezoid has an area of 70 in.^{2} and bases of 8 in. and 6 in. What is its height in inches?

(continued)

Math Thematics, Book 2
Teacher's Resource Book, Modules 5 and 6

Name _____ Date _____

Find each square root. If the square root is not an integer, name the two consecutive integers it lies between.

5. $\sqrt{900}$

6. $\sqrt{33}$

For Questions 7–10, use the right prism shown at the right.

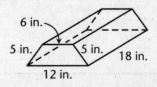

6 in.   5 in.   5 in.   18 in.   12 in.

7. What kind of right prism is this?

8. How many faces, edges, and vertices does the prism have?

9. Sketch a net for the prism.

10. If each base has an area of 36 in.^{2}, what is the surface area of the prism?

11. Use π to write an expression for the exact area of the circle. Then use 3.14 or the π key on your calculator to find the approximate area. Round your answer to the nearest hundredth.

15 mm

Find the approximate radius of a circle with each area. Use 3.14 for π. Round your answer to the nearest hundredth.

12. $A = 9\pi$ in.^{2}

13. $A = 120$ cm^2

MODULE 6　　　　　　　　　　**EXTENDED EXPLORATION LABSHEET** $\mathbf{E^2}$

Map of the Central Region of the United States
(Use with the Extended Exploration on page 434.)

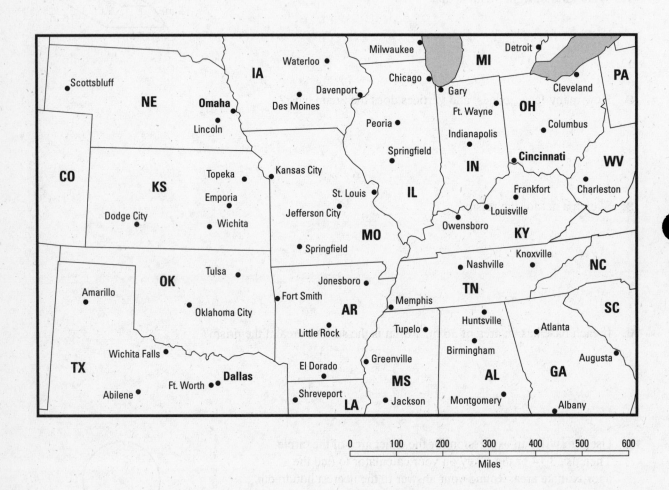

Solution Guide: Textbook E²

For use with E² on textbook page 434

Locating the Hub

This is an open-ended problem that can be approached in many ways. All of the *Math Thematics Assessment Scales* can be used to assess students' solutions, but the problem does not provide much opportunity to use mathematical language or different representations, so you may not want to use the Mathematical Language and Representations Scales.

The sample response below shows part of a student's solution.

Partial Solution

First, I went to the library and found an atlas that had a map with Omaha, Cincinnati, and Dallas on it. I made a copy of the map and drew the triangle with these cities at its vertices on it.

I decided that the best place to locate the hub is at one of the larger cities inside the triangle. I decided the hub should be inside the triangle because I wanted to keep the sum of the distances from the hub to each of the major cities as small as possible.

The next thing I did was to use the scale on the map to find the distance from each of the possible hubs to each of the three major cities. For example, the scale is 6.5 cm = 500 mi and the distance from Omaha to Springfield, IL, on the map is 4.5 cm, so

$$\frac{500}{6.5} = \frac{x}{4.5} \qquad x \approx 346 \text{ mi}$$
$$6.5x = 2250$$

The cities I chose, their populations, and their distance from each of the three major cities are listed in the table. I looked up the populations in an almanac.

	Kansas City, Missouri 435,146	Saint Louis, Missouri 396,685	Springfield, Illinois 105,227	Tulsa, Oklahoma 367,302	Fort Smith, Arkansas 72,798	Springfield, Missouri 140,494	Jefferson City, Missouri 35,481
Cincinnati	534	305	279	660	603	492	412
Dallas	450	549	618	244	221	358	481
Omaha	160	351	346	344	416	313	267
Total miles	1144	1205	1243	1248	1240	1163	1160

I decided that it is also important to keep the lengths of the three flights as close to each other as possible. My recommendation is to use Springfield, Missouri, as the hub. It isn't as large as Kansas City, but it is close to Branson, Missouri, which is a major entertainment center and that might help attract passengers to the airline.

Name _____ Date _____

Alternate E²
For use with Module 6

Tangram

The Situation

The tangram puzzle was introduced in western countries during the first half of the 19th century. The geometric pieces, or *tans*, are combined to form shapes, such as a running man at the right. The tangram is very simple in that it has only seven pieces, but these pieces can be combined in an extraordinary number of ways.

The Problem

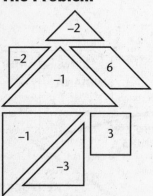

The seven tans, shown on the left, have been given point values. The points are added to find the total point value for the shape formed. Use the tans to create a parallelogram with a value of –2. Then trace the parallelogram that has the greatest point value and the one that has the least point value.

Something to Think About
- How many parallelograms are possible?
- Is there a way to organize your work to find all possible combinations?

Present Your Results
Create a display of your results. Discuss the problem solving strategies you used. Which strategy was most helpful?

Solution Guide: Alternate E²

MODULE 6

For use with Module 6

Tangram

The Problem Solving, Representations, Mathematical Language, and Presentation Scales of the *Math Thematics Assessment Scales* should be used to assess student work. Expect most students to sketch the parallelograms. Organizing the sketches is an important aspect of this E² and will help students find the solution.

The sample response below shows part of a student's solution.

Partial Solution

I began to solve this problem by putting together different tangram pieces to form parallelograms. I realized that I needed a more organized way to find all combinations. I decided to see if I could make any parallelograms with just one tan. Then I would try to make a parallelogram with two pieces, then three pieces, and so on until I used all seven pieces. My parallelograms and the total point value of each are given below.

Using 1 tan

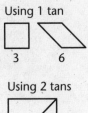

3   6

Using 2 tans

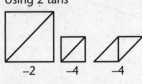

−2   −4   −4

Using 3 tans

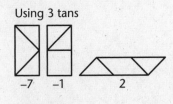

−7   −1   2

Using 4 tans

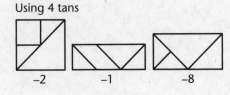

−2   −1   −8

Using 5 tans

−2

Using 6 tans

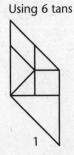

1

Using 7 tans

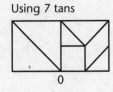

0

I found three different parallelograms with a value of −2, but there may be more. The greatest value I found was 6 using the parallelogram piece only. The least value I found was −8 using four tans (see the drawing above).

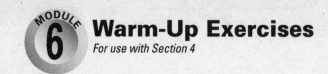

Warm-Up Exercises

For use with Section 4

Use a protractor to find the measure of the angles in each figure.

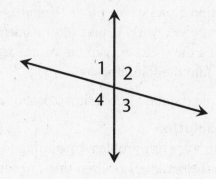

1. **a.** $m\angle 1 =$ _____

b. $m\angle 2 =$ _____

c. $m\angle 3 =$ _____

d. $m\angle 4 =$ _____

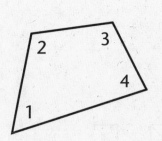

2. **a.** $m\angle 1 =$ _____

b. $m\angle 2 =$ _____

c. $m\angle 3 =$ _____

d. $m\angle 4 =$ _____

ANSWERS

1. a. $m\angle 1 = 74°$ b. $m\angle 2 = 106°$ c. $m\angle 3 = 74°$ d. $m\angle 4 = 106°$
2. a. $m\angle 1 = 60°$ b. $m\angle 2 = 111°$ c. $m\angle 3 = 104°$ d. $m\angle 4 = 84°$

Name _____ Date _____

Build a Wing (Use with Question 1 on page 435 and Question 12 on page 438.)

Construct the bases.

First Cut out two $1\frac{1}{2}$ in. × 5 in. bases.

Then Draw support lines at 1 in. intervals on both bases.

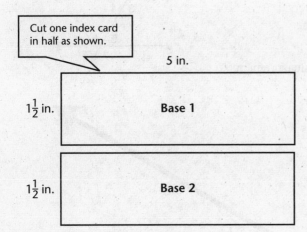

Cut one index card in half as shown.

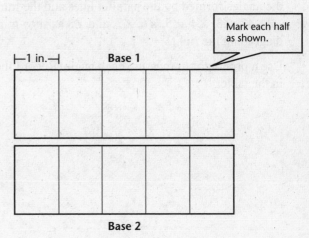

Mark each half as shown.

Construct the supports.

First Cut out four $1\frac{1}{2}$ in. × 2 in. supports.

Then Fold $\frac{1}{4}$ in. tabs on each support.

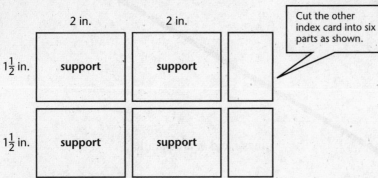

Cut the other index card into six parts as shown.

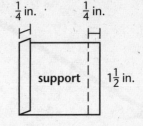

Construct Wing 1.

First Tape one end of a support to a support line on Base 1. Wrap tape around the tab and the base to secure the support. Repeat for the other three supports.

Then Tape the free ends of the supports to Base 2.

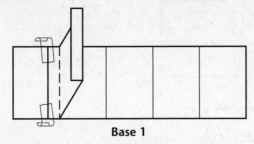

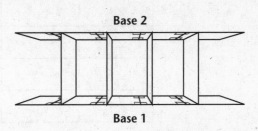

MODULE 6   **LABSHEET 4B**

Transversals and Parallel Lines (Use with Questions 8 and 9 on page 437.)

Directions

- Draw a transversal through the two parallel lines. Then label the angles formed by the parallel lines and the transversal ∠1, ∠2, ∠3, ∠4, ∠5, ∠6, ∠7, and ∠8 as shown in the diagram at the right.

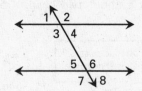

- Use a protractor to measure each angle. Record the measurements in the table.

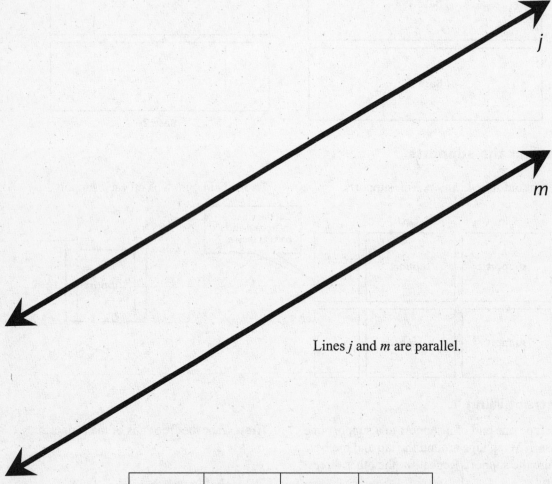

Lines *j* and *m* are parallel.

Angle	Measure	Angle	Measure
∠1		∠2	
∠3		∠4	
∠5		∠6	
∠7		∠8	

Math Thematics, Book 2
Teacher's Resource Book, Modules 5 and 6

Name _____   Date _____

Practice and Applications

For use with Section 4

For use with Exploration 1

1. The figure below shows two parallel lines *c* and *d* cut by transversal *t*. Name the angles or the pairs of angles that fit each description.

   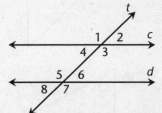

   a. four interior angles

   b. four exterior angles

   c. two pairs of alternate interior angles

   d. two pairs of alternate exterior angles

   e. two pairs of vertical angles

   f. two pairs of corresponding angles

2. Use the figure in Exercise 1. Find the measure of each angle if the measure of $\angle 8$ is 53°.

   a. $\angle 1$ **b.** $\angle 2$ **c.** $\angle 3$

   d. $\angle 4$ **e.** $\angle 5$ **f.** $\angle 6$

3. Use the figure below. The figure shows two parallel lines *a* and *b*. Tell whether each statement is *True* or *False*.

   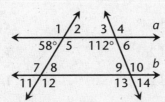

   a. $m\angle 2 = 58°$ **b.** $m\angle 5 = 122°$ **c.** $m\angle 6 = 58°$

   d. $m\angle 5 + m\angle 8 = 180°$ **e.** $m\angle 7 = m\angle 10$ **f.** $m\angle 9 = 68°$

   g. $m\angle 14 = 112°$ **h.** $m\angle 3 = m\angle 9$ **i.** $m\angle 4 = 112°$

   j. $m\angle 1 = m\angle 12$ **k.** $m\angle 8 = 58°$ **l.** $m\angle 11 = m\angle 13$

(continued)

Name _____ Date _____

For use with Exploration 2

4. Find the unknown angle measure in each triangle or quadrilateral.

a.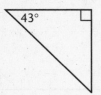
43°

b.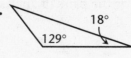
18°
129°

c.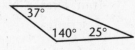
37°
140° 25°

d.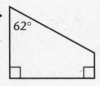
62°

e.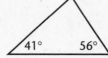
41° 56°

f.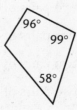
96°
99°
58°

g.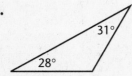
31°
28°

h.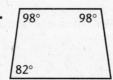
98° 98°
82°

i.
60°
60°

5. The measures of two of the angles of a triangle are given. Find the measure of the third angle of each triangle. Tell whether the triangle is *right*, *acute*, or *obtuse*.

a. 15° and 65°   **b.** 42° and 54°   **c.** 46° and 69°

d. 118° and 41°   **e.** 72° and 26°   **f.** 32° and 58°

g. 38° and 14°   **h.** 59° and 27°   **i.** 11° and 90°

j. 73° and 29°   **k.** 21° and 36°   **l.** 47° and 62°

6. A window is in the shape of a triangle. One of the angles of the triangle measures 32°. The other two angles of the triangle have the same measure. Find each angle measure.

7. Find the sum of the measures of the interior angles of each polygon.

a.

b.

c. a pendedecagon (15-sided polygon)

Study Guide
For use with Section 4

Winging It   Parallel Lines and Angles of Polygons

GOAL   **LEARN HOW TO:** • find relationships among angles formed
                              by parallel lines and a transversal
                            • find the sum of the measures of the angles
                              of a convex polygon

          AS YOU: • examine a model wing
                      • experiment with ways to make a wing rigid

Exploration 1: Angles Formed by a Transversal

Parallel Lines and Transversals

A line that intersects two lines is a **transversal**. When a transversal
intersects two parallel lines, the measures of the eight angles formed are
related. Four of the angles are **exterior angles** because they are outside of
the parallel lines. The other four angles are called **interior angles** because
they are on the inside of, or between, the parallel lines.

A pair of nonadjacent exterior angles found on opposite sides of the
transversal are called **alternate exterior angles**. Nonadjacent pairs of
interior angles found on opposite sides of the transversal are called
alternate interior angles. Angles that have the same position on the two
lines cut by a transversal are called **corresponding angles**. There are also
four pairs of **vertical angles** formed by the intersecting lines. These angle
pairs are directly opposite each other at the intersection of the transversal
and one of the other two lines.

When the two lines intersected by the transversal are parallel, each of the
angle pairs mentioned above is congruent. Recall that congruent angles
have the same measure.

Example

In the figure at the right, line *l* intersects parallel lines
m and *n*. Name all the congruent pairs of angles and
tell why they are congruent.

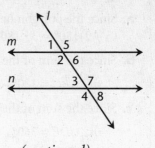

(continued)

Study Guide
For use with Section 4

▨ Sample Response ▨

$\angle 1 \cong \angle 3$, $\angle 2 \cong \angle 4$, $\angle 5 \cong \angle 7$, and $\angle 6 \cong \angle 8$ since corresponding angles are congruent.
$\angle 1 \cong \angle 6$, $\angle 2 \cong \angle 5$, $\angle 3 \cong \angle 8$, and $\angle 4 \cong \angle 7$ since vertical angles are congruent.
$\angle 1 \cong \angle 8$ and $\angle 4 \cong \angle 5$ since alternate exterior angles are congruent.
$\angle 2 \cong \angle 7$ and $\angle 3 \cong \angle 6$ since alternate interior angles are congruent.

Exploration 2: Angles of Polygons

Angles of a Triangle, of a Quadrilateral, and of a Polygon

The sum of the measures of the angles of a triangle is 180°.
The sum of the measures of the angles of a quadrilateral is 360°.

To find the sum of the angles in any polygon, subtract 2 from the total number of sides and multiply this quantity by 180°.

A **diagonal** of a polygon is a segment whose endpoints are two nonconsecutive vertices of the polygon.

Example

Use the figure at the right.

a. Find the sum of the measures of the angles in polygon *ABCDE*.

b. Find the measure of $\angle ABC$ in $\triangle ABC$.

c. Find the measure of $\angle CDE$ in quadrilateral *ACDE*.

d. Name a diagonal of polygon *ABCDE*.

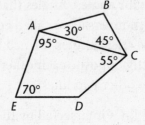

▨ Sample Response ▨

a. Since the polygon has 5 sides, the sum of its angle measures =
$(5 - 2)180° = 3 \cdot 180° = 540°$

b. Since the sum of the measures of the angles of a triangle is 180°,

$$m\angle ABC = 180° - (30° + 45°) = 180° - 75° = 105°$$

c. Since the sum of the measures of the angles of a quadrilateral is 360°,

$$m\angle CDE = 360° - (70° + 95° + 55°) = 360° - 220° = 140°$$

d. $\overline{AC}$ is a diagonal of polygon *ABCDE*.

Name _____ Date _____

MODULE 6 Study Guide: Practice & Application Exercises
For use with Section 4

Exploration 1

The figure at the right shows two parallel lines, *s* and *t*, intersected by transversal *r*. Use this diagram for Exercises 1–12.

Name the angles or pairs of angles that fit each description.

1. four interior angles

2. four exterior angles

3. two pairs of alternate interior angles

4. four pairs of vertical angles

5. two pairs of alternate exterior angles

6. four pairs of corresponding angles

Find the measure of each angle if the measure of ∠3 is 52°.

7. ∠1   **8.** ∠2   **9.** ∠4

10. ∠5   **11.** ∠6   **12.** ∠7

Exploration 2

Find the unknown angle measure in each triangle or quadrilateral.

13.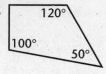

14.

15.

16. One angle of an isosceles triangle has a measure of 94°. Find the measures of the remaining two angles.

Find the sum of the measures of the interior angles of each polygon.

17.

18.

19. tetradecagon (14-sided polygon)

20. chiliagon (1000-sided polygon)

21. The sum of the measures of the interior angles of a polygon is 3960°.

  a. How many sides does this polygon have?

  b. If a polygon is *regular*, it has all sides of the same length and angles of the same measure. If the polygon described is regular, what is the measure of each angle?

Name _____   Date _____

Quick Quiz
For use after Section 4

For Questions 1–3, use the diagram. Lines *r* and *s* are parallel.

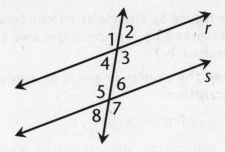

1. Name a pair of vertical angles.

2. Name a pair of alternate interior angles.

3. List four congruent angles in the figure.

4. Find the unknown angle measure in the quadrilateral.

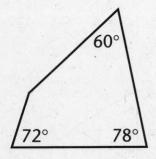

5. Two of the angles of a triangle are 45° and 96°.

   a. What is the measure of the third angle?

   b. Is the triangle *acute*, *obtuse*, or *right*?

Name _____   Date _____

Warm-Up Exercises

For use with Section 5

Write each ratio in two other ways.

1. $3 : 4$

2. $\dfrac{2}{7}$

3. 6 to 1

Solve each proportion.

4. $\dfrac{8}{12} = \dfrac{20}{y}$

5. $\dfrac{x}{4} = \dfrac{5}{6}$

6. $\dfrac{9}{3} = \dfrac{m}{12}$

ANSWERS

1. $\dfrac{3}{4}$; 3 to 4   2. $2 : 7$; 2 to 7   3. $\dfrac{6}{1}$; 6 : 1   4. 30   5. $\dfrac{10}{3}$ 6. 36

MODULE 6   LABSHEET **5A**

Curtiss Jenny (Use with Questions 1–5 on pages 446–448.)

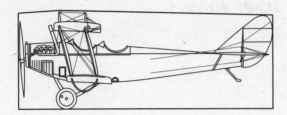

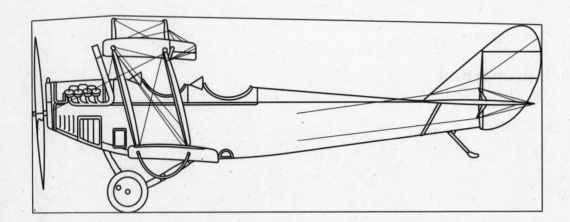

Name _____   Date _____

Practice and Applications

For use with Section 5

For use with Exploration 1

1. Tell whether the polygons in each pair are *similar, congruent,* or *neither.* If the polygons are similar or congruent, write a statement that can be used to identify the corresponding parts.

   a.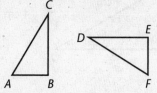

   b.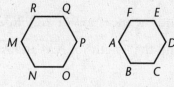

   c.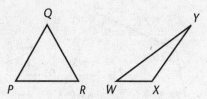

   d.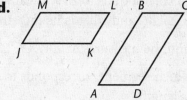

2. A scale drawing of a tree is shown at the right. Each centimeter on the drawing corresponds to 120 cm on the tree. Estimate each measurement of the tree in meters.

   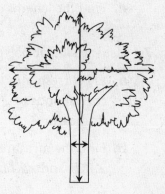

   a. height

   b. width of trunk

   c. center width of foliage

3. A magnifying glass makes an object appear larger. The amount of magnification can be described by using a scale. For each scale, how long does a 6 mm long ant appear to be when seen through the magnifying glass?

   a. 2 : 1   b. 5 : 1   c. 10 : 1

   d. 15 : 1   e. 18 : 1   f. 20 : 1

4. On a map, two cities are 3.5 in. apart. The scale of the map is 1 in. : 60 mi. What is the actual distance between the two cities?

(continued)

Math Thematics, Book 2
Teacher's Resource Book, Modules 5 and 6   **6-49**

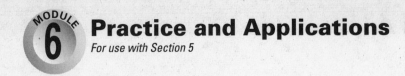

Practice and Applications

For use with Section 5

For use with Exploration 2

5. △MNO is similar to △PQR.

    a. $\overline{OM}$ corresponds to $\overline{RP}$. What segments correspond to $\overline{MN}$ and $\overline{NO}$?

    b. Find the measures of ∠QPR, ∠PRQ, and ∠RQP.

    c. Find the lengths of $\overline{NM}$ and $\overline{MO}$.

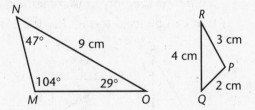

6. Use the similar polygons shown at the right.

    a. $\overline{AB}$ corresponds to $\overline{ZW}$. What angle corresponds to ∠ABC and what is its measure?

    b. Find the measures of ∠WXY, ∠YZW, and ∠XYZ.

    c. Which segment corresponds to $\overline{XY}$? What is its length?

    d. Find the lengths of $\overline{AB}$ and $\overline{AD}$.

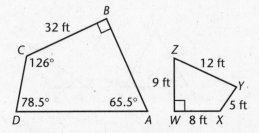

7. Use the similar polygons shown at the right.

    a. $\overline{EH}$ corresponds to $\overline{LI}$. What angle corresponds to ∠EHG? What is its measure?

    b. Find the measures of ∠IJK, ∠JKL, and ∠KLI.

    c. Which segment corresponds to $\overline{GF}$? What is its length?

    d. Find the lengths of $\overline{KL}$ and $\overline{IJ}$.

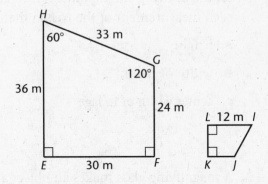

8. Rectangle ABCD is similar to rectangle QRST. The length of one side of rectangle ABCD is three times the width of the rectangle. The length of rectangle QRST is half the length of rectangle ABCD. What is the length of rectangle QRST if the width of rectangle ABCD is 6 cm?

9. Andrea says that all right triangles are similar. Is Andrea correct? Explain why or why not.

Study Guide
For use with Section 5

Barnstorming   Triangles and Similarity

LEARN HOW TO: • identify similar and congruent polygons
• find the scale of a drawing or model
• find the unknown measures in similar figures

AS YOU: • learn about the Curtiss Jenny airplane used by barnstormers
• use scale drawings of a Curtiss Jenny

Exploration 1: Scale Drawings and Similarity

Similar and Congruent Figures

Similar figures have the same shape but not necessarily the same size. Parts of similar figures that match are called **corresponding parts**.

Similar figures that have the same size and shape are *congruent*.

The **scale of a drawing** is the ratio of a length on the drawing to the length of the corresponding part on the actual object.

Example

An architect has created a drawing of a new office building she has designed. The drawing was created using a scale of 1 in. = 15 ft. If the height of the building in the drawing is 6.25 in., what will be the height of the actual building?

Sample Response

Use a proportion.

$$\frac{1 \text{ in.}}{15 \text{ ft}} = \frac{6.25 \text{ in.}}{x \text{ ft}}$$

$$x = 6.25(15)$$

$$= 93.75$$

The building will be 93.75 ft tall.

Study Guide
For use with Section 5

Exploration 2: Unknown Measures in Similar Figures

In similar polygons, the measures of the corresponding angles are equal
and the ratios of the lengths of the corresponding sides are equal.

Example

In the figure at the right, $\triangle ABC$ is similar
to $\triangle DEF$.

a. $\overline{AB}$ corresponds to $\overline{DE}$. What segments
correspond to $\overline{BC}$ and $\overline{AC}$?

b. Find the measures of $\angle D$, $\angle E$, and $\angle F$, and
the lengths of $\overline{EF}$ and $\overline{DF}$.

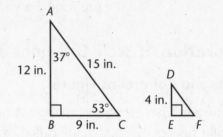

■ Sample Response ■

a. $\overline{EF}$ corresponds to $\overline{BC}$, and $\overline{DF}$ corresponds to $\overline{AC}$.

b. $m\angle D = 37°$, $m\angle E = 90°$, and $m\angle F = 53°$

Since $\dfrac{AB}{DE} = \dfrac{12}{4} = 3$, each side of $\triangle ABC$ is 3 times as long as the corresponding side
of $\triangle DEF$.

So, $DE = 9 \div 3$, or 3 in., and $DF = 15 \div 3$, or 5 in.

The lengths of corresponding sides and the measures of corresponding
angles of congruent polygons are equal.

Example

In the figure at the right, $\triangle ABC \cong \triangle DEF$.

a. Find $m\angle E$.

b. Find EF.

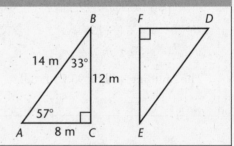

■ Sample Response ■

a. $m\angle E = 33°$ ← $\angle B$ corresponds to $\angle E$, so their measures are equal.

b. $EF = 12$ m   ← $\overline{BC}$ corresponds to $\overline{EF}$, so their measures are equal.

Name _____   Date _____

Study Guide: Practice & Application Exercises

For use with Section 5

6-53

Exploration 1

The amount of magnification under a microscope is given. For each scale, how long does a 2 mm long cell appear to be when seen through a microscope?

1. 15 : 1   **2.** 100 : 1   **3.** 200 : 1

Tell whether the polygons in each pair are *similar, congruent,* or *neither.* If the polygons are similar or congruent, write a statement that can be used to identify the corresponding parts.

4.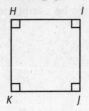

5.

6.

7.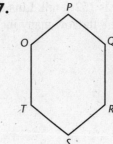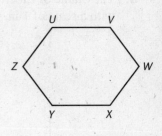

A scale drawing of a box kite is shown at the right. Each centimeter on the drawing corresponds to 20 cm on the box kite. Estimate each measurement on the kite in meters.

8. length   **9.** height   **10.** depth

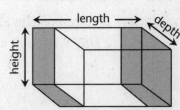

Exploration 2

Trapezoid *ABCD* is similar to trapezoid *EFGH*.

11. $\overline{AB}$ corresponds to $\overline{EF}$. Which segments correspond to $\overline{BC}$, $\overline{CD}$, and $\overline{AC}$, respectively?

12. Find the measures of $\angle A$, $\angle B$, $\angle C$, and $\angle D$.

13. Find the lengths of $\overline{BC}$, $\overline{CD}$, and $\overline{AD}$.

14. Draw two similar pentagons in which the ratio of the corresponding sides is 4 to 1. Explain how you know the pentagons are similar.

Math Thematics, Book 2
Teacher's Resource Book, Modules 5 and 6   **6-53**

Name _____ Date _____

1. Draw two obtuse triangles that are similar but not congruent.

2. The two pentagons shown at the right are similar. Write a statement that can be used to identify the corresponding parts.

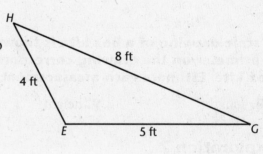

3. The Statue of Liberty is 152 ft tall. Luis drew a scale drawing of the statue with a scale of 1 in. = 8 ft. How many inches tall was his drawing?

4. The two triangles shown at the right are similar.

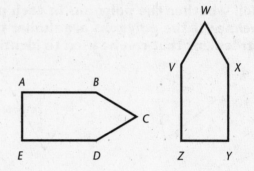

  a. $\overline{IJ}$ corresponds to $\overline{EH}$. What angle corresponds to ∠*IJK*? What is its measure?

  b. Find the lengths of $\overline{JK}$ and $\overline{KI}$.

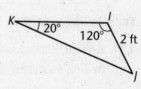

Practice and Applications

For use after Sections 1–5

For use with Section 1

1. Classify each polygon as concave or convex.

a.    **b.** 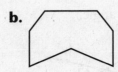   **c.**

2. Find the area of a trapezoid with the given measurements.

a. $b_1 = 4$ in., $b_2 = 7$ in., $h = 8$ in.   **b.** $b_1 = 9$ cm, $b_2 = 5$ cm, $h = 12$ cm

3. Find each unknown dimension or the area.

a. trapezoid   **b.** parallelogram   **c.** trapezoid

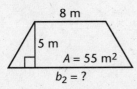   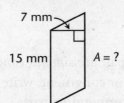   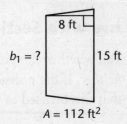

For use with Section 2

4. A box contains 1 red marker and 4 blue markers. Without looking, Danny reaches into the box and pulls out the first marker he touches. He puts the marker back into the box and then his sister Megan reaches into the box, without looking, and pulls out the first marker that she touches. What is the probability that both Danny and Megan pull out blue markers?

For use with Section 3

5. Find each of the following. If the principal square root is not a whole number, find the two consecutive integers it is between.

a. $\sqrt{200}$ **b.** $-\sqrt{225}$ **c.** $\sqrt{121}$ **d.** $-\sqrt{13.5}$

6. Use π to write an expression for the exact area of each circle. Then use 3.14 or the ⬚ₚ key on a calculator to find the approximate area. Round approximate answers to the nearest hundredth.

a. 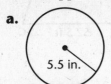   **b.** 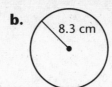   **c.**

(continued)

Name _____   Date _____

For use with Section 4

7. The figure below shows parallel lines $\overleftrightarrow{AB}$ and $\overleftrightarrow{CD}$ cut by transversal $\overleftrightarrow{SW}$. Find the measure of each named angle.

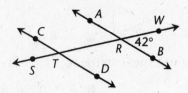

   a. ∠ART   **b.** ∠DTR   **c.** ∠STD

   d. ∠CTR   **e.** ∠CTS   **f.** ∠ARW

For use with Section 5

8. Tell whether the polygons in each pair are *similar*, *congruent*, or *neither*. If the polygons are similar or congruent, write a statement that can be used to identify the corresponding parts.

   a.

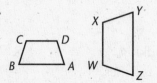

   b.

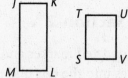

9. On a map, two cities are 4 in. apart. The scale of the map is 1 in. : 75 mi. What is the actual distance between the two cities?

10. The scale 5000 : 1 describes the setting for the magnification on an electron microscope. How long does a 0.003 mm long speck of asbestos appear to be when seen through the electron microscope?

11. Trapezoid *ABCD* is similar to trapezoid *EHGF*.

   a. Find the measures of ∠FGH, ∠GHE, and ∠HEF.

   b. Find the lengths of $\overline{AD}$, $\overline{AB}$, and $\overline{DC}$.

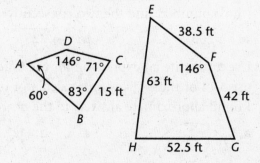

MODULE 6   **PROJECT LABSHEET** **A**

Create a Wild Wing
(Use with Project Questions 1 and 4 on page 458.)

Step 1 Draw a line 2 in. from the top of an $8\frac{1}{2}$ in. by 11 in. sheet of paper. This will be the tail of your Wild Wing.

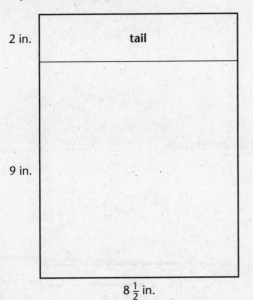

Step 2 Bring the bottom edge of the paper up to meet the line you drew. Fold and crease the paper. Repeat this step three more times.

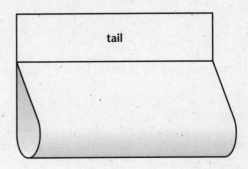

Step 3 To create a rectangular Wild Wing, fold the paper in fourths. Here is one way to do this: first, fold the paper in half, next, open the paper, and then fold each side into the middle.

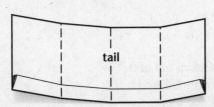

Step 4 Bring the ends together and tape the seam. The folded edge should be in the interior of your Wild Wing.

rectangular Wild Wing

To create a triangular Wild Wing, fold the paper in thirds.

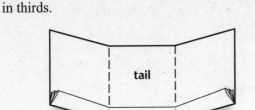

triangular Wild Wing

Name _____   Date _____

For Questions 1 and 2, write and graph an inequality to represent the situation.

1. A cruise ship has a maximum capacity of 360 passengers, but the company will cancel a cruise unless 200 people have made reservations.

2. Sara practices the piano at least 40 min each day.

3. Sketch a trapezoid that has an area of 25 cm^2 and label its dimensions.

4. A dart is equally likely to land in any region of the rectangular target at the right. Find the probability that the dart

   a. will land in the shaded triangle.

   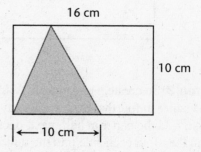

   b. will not land in the shaded triangle.

5. A bag contains 5 tiles: 2 triangles and 3 squares. One tile is taken out of the bag without looking. The number of sides of the tile is recorded, and the tile is returned to the bag. Then the process is repeated once more. The outcome is the sum of the number of sides of the two shapes drawn.

   a. Use a separate sheet of paper. Draw a tree diagram that shows all of the possible outcomes of the experiment.

   b. What is the theoretical probability that the outcome is 7?

Find each square root. If the square root is not an integer, name the two consecutive integers it is between.

6. $\sqrt{180}$

7. $\sqrt{484}$

Math Thematics, Book 2
Teacher's Resource Book, Modules 5 and 6

6-58

Test Form A

For use after Module 6

8. **a.** Sketch a net for the right triangular prism shown below. Label the dimension of each face.

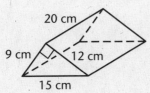

b. Find the surface area of the prism.

Use π to write an expression for the exact area of each circle. Then use 3.14 for π to find each approximate area rounded to the nearest tenth.

9.

60 mm

10.

4 in.

11. Lines *a* and *b* are parallel. Find the measures of angles 1, 2, 3, 4, 5, 6, and 7.

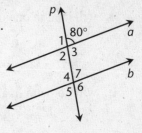

12. 61° and 29° are the measures of two angles of a triangle.

a. Find the measure of the third angle.   **b.** Is the triangle *acute*, *obtuse*, or *right*?

13. What is the sum of the measures of the interior angles of a 12-sided polygon?

14. Quadrilateral *ABCD* is similar to quadrilateral *PLMN*.

a. Find the measures of all the unlabeled line segments.

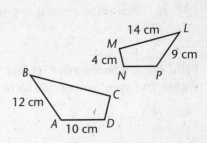

b. If you know the angle measures of quadrilateral *ABCD*, what can you say about the angle measures in quadrilateral *PLMN*?

Name _____   Date _____

For Questions 1 and 2, write and graph an inequality to represent the situation.

1. The load on an elevator ranges from 0 lb to a maximum of 3000 lb.

2. A wild elephant eats at least 500 lb of food per day.

3. Sketch a trapezoid that has an area of 40 cm² and label its dimensions.

4. Find the probability that a small object dropped onto the figure shown at the right

   a. will land in one of the shaded triangles.

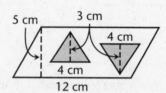

   b. will not land in a shaded triangle.

5. A bag contains 5 tiles: 4 triangles, and 1 pentagon. One tile is taken out of the bag without looking. The number of sides of the tile is recorded, and the tile is returned to the bag. Then the process is repeated once more. The outcome is the sum of the number of sides of the two shapes drawn.

   a. Use a separate sheet of paper. Draw a tree diagram that shows all of the possible outcomes of the experiment.

   b. What is the theoretical probability that the outcome is 8?

Find each square root. If the square root is not an integer, name the two consecutive integers it is between.

6. $\sqrt{60}$ 7. $\sqrt{676}$

Test Form B
For use after Module 6

8. a. Sketch a net for the right triangular prism below. Label the dimension of each face.

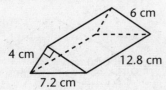

6 cm
4 cm
12.8 cm
7.2 cm

b. Find the surface area of the prism.

Use π to write an expression for the exact area of each circle. Then use 3.14 for π to find each approximate area rounded to the nearest tenth.

9.

10 ft

10.

18.2 cm

11. Lines *a* and *b* are parallel. Find the measures of angles 1, 2, 3, 4, 5, 6, and 7.

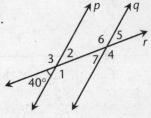

p *q*
6 5 *r*
3 2 7 4
40° 1

12. 48° and 22° are the measures of two angles of a triangle.

a. Find the measure of the third angle.

b. Is the triangle *acute*, *obtuse*, or *right*?

13. What is the sum of the measures of the interior angles of a 10-sided polygon?

14. Quadrilateral *ABCD* is similar to quadrilateral *XZYW*.

a. Find the measures of all the unlabeled line segments.

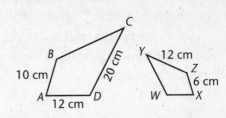

C
B
10 cm
20 cm
A 12 cm D
Y 12 cm
Z
6 cm
W X

b. If you know the angle measures of quadrilateral *ABCD*, what can you say about the angle measures in quadrilateral *XZYW*?

Name _____ Date _____

1. Which is represented by the graph?

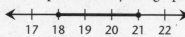

17 18 19 20 21 22

   a. Sue has no more than $21 in the bank.
   b. Only students between the ages of 18 and 21 should apply.
   c. Each of the 21 snakes is at least 18 inches long.
   d. The baby weighs at least 18 lb but less than 21 lb.

2. Suppose a coin is tossed three times in a row and the results are recorded in order. What is the probability that the first and third tosses are heads?

   a. $\frac{1}{8}$ **b.** $\frac{1}{4}$ **c.** $\frac{3}{8}$ **d.** $\frac{1}{2}$

3. Estimate $\sqrt{14}$ to the nearest tenth.
   a. 3.6   **b.** 3.7
   c. 3.8   **d.** 3.9

4. Find the area of this trapezoid.

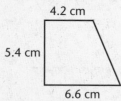

4.2 cm

5.4 cm

6.6 cm

   a. 19.5 cm^2 **b.** 25.16 cm^2
   c. 29.16 cm^2 **d.** 33.6 cm^2

5. The longest suspension bridge in the world, the Humber Estuary Bridge in England, is 4626 ft long. A model of it is 18 in. long with towers 2.07 in. tall. To the nearest foot, what is the actual height of the towers?
   a. 532 ft   **b.** 549 ft
   c. 586 ft   **d.** 624 ft

6. Find the surface area of the right triangular prism.

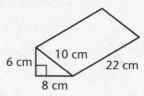

6 cm   10 cm   22 cm
8 cm

   a. 10,560 cm^2 **b.** 624 cm^2
   c. 576 cm^2 **d.** 528 cm^2

7. The probability that a certain basketball player will make a free throw is 82%. What is the approximate probability that she will miss 2 free throws in a row?
   a. 3%   **b.** 8%
   c. 23%   **d.** 36%

8. Find the area of a circle with a diameter of 12 in.
   a. 12π in.^{2} **b.** 36π in.^{2}
   c. 60π in.^{2} **d.** 144π in.^{2}

9. If $\triangle ABC \sim \triangle MNL$, find NL.

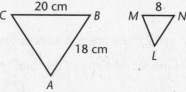

20 cm
C   B   M   8   N
           18 cm   L
      A

   a. 7.2 cm   **b.** 7.8 cm
   c. 8.3 cm   **d.** 8.8 cm

10. If lines p and q are parallel, what is $m\angle 6$?

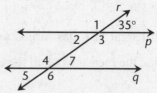

r
1   35°
2   3   p
4   7
5   6   q

   a. 35°   **b.** 70°
   c. 145°   **d.** 155°

Name _____ Date _____

Three sisters, Anastasia, Beulah, and Chrysilla, had lived for many years in different parts of the world. Anastasia had settled in Switzerland, where she lived in a blue and white A-frame chateau high in the Swiss Alps. Beulah lived in Mexico in a traditional flat-roofed adobe hacienda. Chrysilla lived in Kansas in a simple farm house with a peaked roof.

Now, after many years apart, the sisters have decided to buy some land in Delaware. They plan to build a house large enough for all of them to live in together. But each sister wants the house to look like the one in which she has lived.

The three sisters decide to solve the problem by choosing the design which is most efficient at holding heat. They have reasoned that the house with the smallest surface-area-to-volume ratio will be the one with the most heat-efficient design. So, they want to find the surface area and volume of each house design, and then calculate the surface-area-to-volume ratio.

Hint: To find the volume of a right prism, multiply the area of the base by the height.

1. Use the dimensions, given in feet, of the house plans shown below to calculate the surface area, volume, and surface-area-to-volume ratio of each house.

Anastasia's Plan

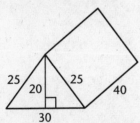

Beulah's Plan

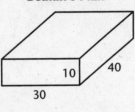

Chrysilla's Plan

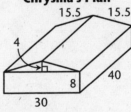

2. Which house should they build?

3. Chrysilla decides that they should build a bigger house, regardless of the plan they use. She wants the width of the base to be 45 ft instead of 30 ft. The remaining dimensions should be in the same scale as the original structure. Re-draw each house design, and calculate the new dimensions for each house.

4. Beulah says they will need to calculate the surface-area-to-volume ratio all over again, because the ratio changes when the dimensions change. Is Beulah right?

Name _____ Date _____

Cumulative Test
For use after Modules 5 and 6

Write each rate as a unit rate.

1. $\dfrac{\$8.64}{2.4\text{ lb}}$

2. $\dfrac{14°}{3\text{ hr}}$

3. Make a stem-and-leaf plot for the following data.

Games Won by American League Baseball Teams, 2006

New York	97	Minnesota	96	Oakland	93
Toronto	87	Detroit	95	Los Angeles	89
Boston	86	Chicago	90	Texas	80
Baltimore	70	Cleveland	78	Seattle	78
Tampa Bay	61	Kansas City	62		

4. Find the range, the mean, the median, and the mode of games won.

Use the histogram for Exercises 5 and 6.

5. How many Nobel prize winners for 1997 were less than 60 years old?

6. Which of the following information can you get from this histogram: the median of the data, the range of the data, the mean of the data, or the mode of the data? Explain.

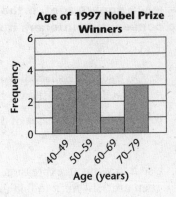

Solve each proportion.

7. $\dfrac{x}{18} = \dfrac{21}{40}$

8. $\dfrac{6}{11} = \dfrac{150}{y}$

9. **a.** Use the box-and-whisker plot to estimate the median number of countries who participated in the Winter Olympics.

b. About what fraction of the Winter Olympics had more than 49 countries participating?

Number of Countries Participating in Twentieth Century Winter Olympic Games

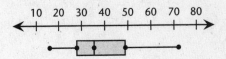

10. Write $\dfrac{25}{43}$ as a percent. Round to the nearest tenth of a percent.

Solve for each unknown number.

11. 18% of a number is 9.

12. A number is 72% of 400.

13. Write an example of a situation that could be represented by this graph, and then write the inequality.

```
<────●──────────────●────
    21              65
```

Cumulative Test
For use after Modules 5 and 6

14. Find the probability that a small object dropped onto this right triangle will land on the shaded part of the figure.

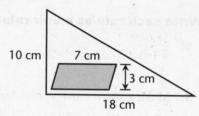

10 cm   7 cm   3 cm   18 cm

15. A bag contains 2 white marbles and 3 blue marbles. Three marbles are removed from the bag one after another. After each marble is removed, its color is recorded and the marble is put back into the bag before the next marble is removed.

   a. Use a separate sheet of paper. Draw a tree diagram that shows all of the possible outcomes of this experiment.

   b. What is the theoretical probability that a blue marble is drawn first, followed by two whites? Express your answer as a fraction, a decimal, and a percent.

Find each square root. If the square root is not an integer, name the two consecutive integers it is between.

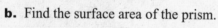

16. $\sqrt{115}$ 17. $\sqrt{900}$

18. **a.** On a separate sheet of paper, sketch a net for the right triangular prism shown. Label the dimension of each face.

   b. Find the surface area of the prism.

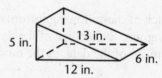

5 in.   13 in.   6 in.   12 in.

19. Use π to write an expression for the exact area of a circle with radius length 2.7 in. Then use 3.14 for π to find the approximate area rounded to the nearest tenth.

20. 19° and 110° are two angles of a triangle.

   a. Find the measure of the third angle.   **b.** Is the triangle *acute, obtuse,* or *right*?

21. △*ABC* Is similar to △*JKL*. Find the measures of all the unlabeled segments.

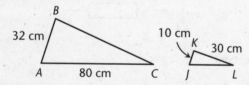

B   32 cm   A   80 cm   C   10 cm   K   30 cm   J   L

22. Lines *a* and *b* are parallel. Find the measures of angles 1, 2, 3, 4, 5, 6, and 7.

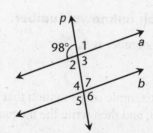

98°

MODULE 5 Answer Key
For use with Module 5

MODULE 5

Diagnostic Test (p. 5-2)

1. $0.75/\text{can}$

2. $\dfrac{15}{40} = \dfrac{x}{2000}$

3. **a. Contributions to a Charity**

```
 2 | 0 0 5
 3 |
 4 | 0 5
 5 | 0
 6 |
 7 |
 8 | 0
 9 |
10 | 0
```

4 | 0 represents a $40 contribution

b. mean = $47.50; median = $42.50; mode = $20; range = $80

c. Sample Response: Since the mean is affected by the two large contributions and the mode is equal to the smallest contribution, the median is most representative of the contributions. So I would give a contribution that is close to the median, say $40 or $45.

4. Sample Response: Should a new swimming facility be built for our community? If a new swimming facility were built, how often would you use it?

5. histogram

6. **a.**

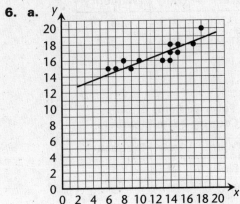

b. Answers will vary. Sample Response: When $x = 12$, y is about 16.5.

7. $\dfrac{x}{14} = \dfrac{1.5}{2}$

$2x = 14 \cdot 1.5$

$2x = 21$

$x = 10.5$

8. **a.** 10 hr **b.** about 25%

9. A

10. **a.** 30 **b.** 12.8

11. 88.2%

12. D

13. 250%

SECTION 1

Practice and Applications (p. 5-9)

1. **a.** 8.5 min/mi **b.** 23 mi/gal **c.** $2.80/lb
   d. 8 servings/pan **e.** $0.07/min **f.** $0.89/bunch
   g. 6.4 min/mi **h.** $4.50/lb **i.** 5.8 gal/min
   j. 10 servings/pan **k.** $2.59/bunch
   l. 12 servings/pan **m.** 28 mi/gal **n.** $12.75/hr
   o. 23.5 km/L

2. 55 lb/day = 385 lb/7 days

3. about 8824 people/mi^2

4. **a.**

Time (min)	4	8	40	80	960
Distance (mi)	0.5	1	5	10	120

b. 16 hr

5. **a.**

Time (sec)	1	5	20	30	50
Distance (ft)	6	30	120	180	300

b. 300 ft

6. **a. Number of Minutes Students Spent Reading**

```
 7 | 6 9
 8 | 3 3 5 6 8 8 9 9 9
 9 | 0 1 2 2 4 6 9
10 | 0 0
```

8 | 5 = 85 min

b. 24; 89.45; 89; 88 and 89 **c.** 89 min

7. **a.** median = 41.5, modes = 25, 48 **b.** Sample Response: There are gaps between 37 and 46 and between 48 and 60; there are clusters around 25 and 48. **c.** Sample Response: The range does not change because 51 is neither the least nor greatest value in the data set.

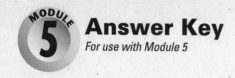

Answer Key
For use with Module 5

Study Guide Exercises (p. 5-13)

1. $4.60/box

2. 27 mi/gal

3. 6.25¢/min

4. 0.12 mi/min

5. 80 to 1, 80:1, $\frac{80}{1}$

6. The ratio $\frac{$2.50}{2 \text{ kg}}$ is not a unit rate because it does not represent cost for a single unit.

7. 60 gal

8. company Y

9. **a.** **Ages of People Enrolled in Art Classes at the Museum**

   ```
   1 | 5 5 8 9
   2 | 3 8
   3 | 4
   4 | 5
   5 |
   6 | 3 5 5 7
   7 | 0
   ```

   1 | 5 represents 15 years

   b. range: 55; median: 34; modes: 15 and 65
   c. Sample Response: No. The youngest age, 15, is only 3 years younger than the next age, 18. The oldest age, 70, is only 3 years older than the previous age, 67. **d.** Sample Response: 14 would increase the range from 55 to 56 and 15 would not affect the mode, which is already 15.

Quick Quiz (p. 5-14)

1. about $4.83/lb

2. 6.8 hr or 6 hr 48 min

3. range: 33 points; median: 16.5 points; mode: 17 points

4. Answers will vary. Check students' plots.

SECTION 2

Practice and Applications (p. 5-18)

1. Answers may vary.

2. Answers may vary.

3. Answers may vary.

4. Sample Response: There were enough spaces to let each space represent one person.

5. Sample Response: I found the greatest number of tally marks; I found the longest bar.

6. Answers may vary.

7. **a.** 10 min **b.** about 14 students **c.** greater than **d.** Sample Response: No; the histogram only gives a range of time, not exact times.

8. **a.** Sample Response: a histogram; the data is grouped in intervals, not distinct categories.
   b. Sample Response: The community can use the results to decide what age-appropriate equipment to put in the playground. They can also use it to decide whether or not to even build a playground.

Study Guide Exercises (p. 5-22)

1. Sample Response: What time of day do you most often visit the library? How many days per week do you visit the library? What is your favorite morning beverage? What do you like to eat for lunch?

2. No; Sample Response: Adventure and comedy are too close to determine which is the favorite.

3. **Scores on an English Grammar Test**

Score	Tally	Frequency
91–100	JHT III	8
81–90	JHT III	8
71–80	JHT I	6
61–70	II	2

4. **Favorite Color of Cross Country Team Members**

Color	Tally	Frequency
Blue	III	3
Red	III	3
Yellow	III	3
Green	III	3
Orange	I	1

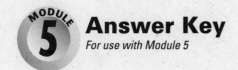

Answer Key

For use with Module 5

5. less than
6. 30 students
7. No; Sample Response: A histogram displays data in intervals. You would need to know exact numbers to determine the mode.

Quick Quiz (p. 5-23)

1. Sample Response: Which of the following, mathematics, science, English, or social studies, is your favorite subject in school?
2. Check students' work.
3.

Number of CDs bought	0	1	2	3	4	5	6	12
Frequency	3	4	4	2	2	1	1	1

4. 15 students

SECTION 3

Practice and Applications (p. 5-30)

1. 28 g
2. 320 g
3. 525 lb
4. **a.** 52.5 **b.** 24 **c.** 27 **d.** 12 **e.** 17 **f.** 5 **g.** 12.5 **h.** 30 **i.** 8.1 **j.** 12 **k.** 40 **l.** 8.5 **m.** 45 **n.** 21 **o.** 45
5. **a.** 262.5 **b.** 105 gal **c.** 750 loaves **d.** 360 lb
6. Sample Response: scatter plot A, because more of the points lie close to the line
7. **a.** Sample Response: about $200,000 **b.** Sample Response: One house is older than the other.
8. **a.** $90 **b.** $5 **c.** $35 **d.** $85

Study Guide Exercises (p. 5-34)

1. $g = 12$
2. $k = 14$
3. $c = 30$
4. $x = 8.4$
5. 196 oz
6. $3.75
7. Sample Response: scatter plot A; approximately half of the points are

plotted above the line and the other half are below it.

8. about 3.5 in.
9. 6 years
10. 10 years
11. range = 8
12. 15 members

Quick Quiz (p. 5-35)

1. 104
2. 42
3.

Winning Distances for Men's Olympic Discus

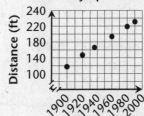

4. about 240
5. **a.** range: about 14 ft **b.** median: about 9 ft

Mid-Module Quiz (p. 5-36)

1. $4/lb
2. 0.004 in./min
3. **a. Home Runs for Triple Crown Winners**

```
0 | 9
1 | 4  4  8
2 | 8
3 | 1  2  6  9
4 | 2  4  8  9  9
5 | 2
```

3 | 6 means 36 home runs

b. range = 43; median = 36; modes = 14 and 49

4. **a.** 14 drivers **b.** 29 speeds **c.** No; you can tell only that the fastest winning speed is in the interval from 180 mi/hr to 189 mi/hr.

5. $5\frac{7}{9}$
6. 24

7. a–b.

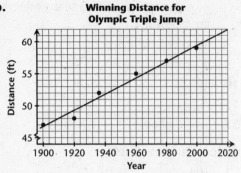

Winning Distance for Olympic Triple Jump

c. Answers will vary. Sample Response: about 62 ft

8. a. median = 8 **b.** range = 4

SECTION 4

Practice and Applications (p. 5-40)

1. Sample Response: about 60%

2. a. $\frac{8}{16}$ or $\frac{1}{2}$ **b.** about 50%

3. Sample Responses are given.
  a. about 90% **b.** about 33% **c.** about 33%
  d. about 75% **e.** about 40% **f.** about 50%
  g. about 85% **h.** about 40% **i.** about 33%
  j. about 20% **k.** about 12% **l.** about 25%

4. about 64%; about 47%

5. a. 83.3% **b.** 40% **c.** 75% **d.** 62.5% **e.** 70%
  f. 46.9% **g.** 26.7% **h.** 32.5% **i.** 16.7%
  j. 77.8% **k.** 31.3% **l.** 20%

6. about 20%

7. 450 students; the number of students can be found by solving $\frac{44}{100} = \frac{198}{x}$.

8. a. 50 **b.** 60 **c.** 850 **d.** 25.5 **e.** 180 **f.** 3.68
  g. 260 **h.** 392 **i.** 36 **j.** 84 **k.** 150 **l.** 125
  m. 16 **n.** 500 **o.** 112 **p.** 90 **q.** 224 **r.** 3
  s. 360 **t.** 85.2 **u.** 30 **v.** 150 **w.** 165 **x.** 57.4

9. $6.43

10. $18

11. 240 Calories

12. 600 students

Study Guide Exercises (p. 5-44)

1–5. Sample Responses are given.

1. about 50%

2. about 33%

3. about 75%

4. about 100%

5. about 33%

6. about 20%

7. 66.7%

8. 60%

9. 22%

10. 77.8%

11. about 71%

12. 24%

13. 650

14. 11.88

15. 48

16. 100

17. 25

18. 112.5

19. 20

20. 40

Quick Quiz (p. 5-45)

1. Sample Response: 67% (from $\frac{28}{42}$ or $\frac{30}{45}$);
  63% (from $\frac{25}{40}$); 60% (from $\frac{27}{40}$)

2. about 75% (from $\frac{60}{80}$)

3. 31.1%

4. 180

5. 24

SECTION 5

Practice and Applications (p. 5-47)

1. a. $\frac{2}{3}$, $0.6\overline{6}$, $66\frac{2}{3}\%$ **b.** $\frac{1}{2}$, 0.5, 50% **c.** $\frac{3}{5}$, 0.6, 60% **d.** $\frac{9}{25}$, 0.36, 36% **e.** $\frac{1}{3}$, $0.3\overline{3}$, $33\frac{1}{3}\%$
  f. $\frac{7}{10}$, 0.7, 70% **g.** $\frac{3}{4}$, 0.75, 75% **h.** $\frac{37}{100}$, 0.37, 37% **i.** $\frac{19}{20}$, 0.95, 95%

2. a. 14% **b.** 75% **c.** 60% **d.** 76% **e.** 87.5%
  f. 48.5% **g.** 37.5% **h.** 16% **i.** 36%

Answer Key
For use with Module 5

3. a. 15% **b.** 68% **c.** 25% **d.** $11\frac{1}{9}$% **e.** 32%
f. $66\frac{2}{3}$% **g.** 50% **h.** 7% **i.** 50%

4. a. 180 students **b.** 150 students
c. 90 students

5. Sample Response: about 480,000

6. 150%

7. a. 25% **b.** 30% **c.** 55% **d.** 75% **e.** 90%
f. 80% **g.** 95% **h.** 20% **i.** 100% **j.** 35%
k. 130% **l.** 85% **m.** 190% **n.** 110% **o.** 15%
p. 45% **q.** 125% **r.** 250% **s.** 165% **t.** 200%
u. 140% **v.** 120% **w.** 160% **x.** 175%
y. 225% **z.** 150%

8. 117 beats per minute

9. 91 beats per minute

10. 98 beats per minute

Study Guide Exercises (p. 5-51)

1. $\frac{2}{5}$, 0.4, 40%

2. $\frac{12}{36}$ or $\frac{1}{3}$, $0.\overline{3}$, 33%

3. $\frac{8}{40}$ or $\frac{1}{5}$, 0.2, 20%

4. $\frac{18}{100}$ or $\frac{9}{50}$, 0.18, 18%

5. $\frac{1}{20}$, 0.05, 5%

6. $\frac{54}{210}$ or $\frac{9}{35}$, about 0.257, about 25.7%

7. $\frac{3}{4}$, 0.75, 75%

8. $\frac{258}{2000}$ or $\frac{129}{1000}$, 0.129, 12.9%

9. $33\frac{1}{3}$%

10. 25%

11. 6%

12. $66\frac{2}{3}$%

13. Sample Response: about 170 students

14. 4 or 5 A's

15. 9 or 10 times

16. 120%

17. 40%

18. 57.5%

19. 200%

20. 135%

21. 100%

22. 500%

23. 120%

24. 210%

Quick Quiz (p. 5-52)

1. 0.310

2. about 7

3. 11.8%

4. 140%

5. 250%

END-OF-MODULE RESOURCES AND ASSESSMENTS

Practice and Applications, Sections 1–5 (p. 5-53)

1. a. 9.2 min/mi **b.** 27 mi/gal **c.** $0.08/min
d. 29.4 km/L **e.** 9.5 min/mi **f.** $3.75/lb
g. $14.60/hr **h.** $0.68/bunch **i.** 7.5 min/mi

2. 3.6 mi/hr

3. a. Sample Response: a gap between 69 and 80; a cluster around 90 **b.** 31 **c.** 90; 91

4.

	Tally	Frequency
6	III	3
7	II	2
8	IIII	5
9	III	3
10	II	2

5. Sample Response: How often do you recycle? What do you find most inconvenient about recycling?

6. a. 21 **b.** No; Sample Response: You can only tell how many children are between the ages of 6 and 8.

7. a. 14 **b.** 28.8 **c.** 15 **d.** 25 **e.** 5 **f.** 3.6 **g.** 56
h. 5 **i.** 27 **j.** 1.5 **k.** 99 **l.** 5

8. 48 lb

9. about 10

10. about 15

11. a. about 50% **b.** about 10% **c.** about 80%
d. about 25% **e.** about 75% **f.** about 40%

12. a. 46.7% **b.** 20% **c.** 25% **d.** 55% **e.** 92%
f. 53.8%

13. a. 120 **b.** 140 **c.** 90 **d.** 27.3 **e.** 54 **f.** 9

14. $62

15. a. 65% **b.** 88% **c.** 25%

16. about 152,000

17. a. 135% **b.** 600% **c.** 150% **d.** 100%
e. 175% **f.** 320%

Test Form A (p. 5-57)

1. 84 km/hr

2. $4.50/lb

**3. Number of Hospitals per State
in 10 Selected States**

```
3 | 7 9
4 | 0 3
5 | 0 4 7
6 | 2 2
7 | 0
```
4 | 1 represents 41 hospitals

4. range = 33; median = 51; mode = 62

5. Sample Response: 830 to 840

6. No; you can tell only that the slowest time is
in the interval from 16 hr to 16 hr 59 sec.

7. $y = 18.75$

8. $z = 16$

9. a. about 9.5 days **b.** 1148 ft

10. a–b.

c. Answers will vary. Sample Response:
When $x = 8$, y is about 7.5.

11. a. 29 medals **b.** about 15 countries

12. about 65%

13. about 20%

14. about 75%

15. 38.5%

16. 87.8%

17. 450

18. 138

19. 193.75%

Test Form B (p. 5-59)

1. 67.5 km/hr

2. $4.55/lb

**3. Number of State Legislators
in Selected States**

```
 7 | 6
 8 |
 9 |
10 |
11 | 2
12 |
13 | 2 2 5 8
14 | 8 9
15 | 0
16 |
17 |
18 | 7
```
14 | 8 represents 148 legislators

4. range = 111; median = 136.5; mode = 132

5. 20 years

6. No; you can tell only that the fastest time
was at least 8 days but less than 9 days.

7. $x = 55$

8. $z = 9$

9. a. about 4 years **b.** about 7.5 in./week

10. a–b.

c. Answers will vary. Sample Response:
When $y = 8$, x is about 21.

Answer Key

For use with Module 5

11. a. 27 points per game **b.** about 9 players
12. 10%
13. 30%
14. 90%
15. 91.7%
16. 56.5%
17. 350
18. 234
19. 156.25%

Standardized Test (p. 5-61)

1. c
2. b
3. b
4. b
5. a
6. c
7. c
8. c
9. d
10. a
11. a
12. b

Performance Assessment (p. 5-62)

1. Ricky should sit 4 ft from the fulcrum.

2.

```
          16 cm        | 4 cm
      ┌────────────────┴──────┐
                    10 cm  | 4 cm
    (14 g)          ┌──────┴──────┐
                             3 cm | 3 cm
               (16 g)        ┌────┴────┐
                           ⬡20 g   ⬡20 g
```

MODULE 6

Diagnostic Test (p. 6-2)

1. $-5 \leq t$, where t is a temperature during the day.

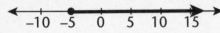

2. B
3. B
4. C
5. D
6. 12
7. 6 and 7
8.

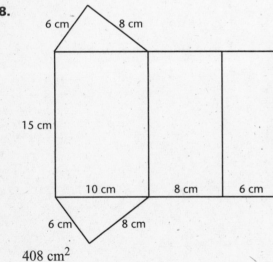

  408 cm^2

9. B
10. **a.** any two of the following: $\angle 2$, $\angle 3$, $\angle 4$, or $\angle 7$ **b.** $\angle 1$ and $\angle 8$, $\angle 2$ and $\angle 5$, $\angle 4$ and $\angle 7$, or $\angle 3$ and $\angle 6$ **c.** $\angle 1$ and $\angle 3$, $\angle 5$ and $\angle 7$, $\angle 2$ and $\angle 4$, or $\angle 6$ and $\angle 8$ **d.** $\angle 1$ and $\angle 6$ or $\angle 4$ and $\angle 5$
11. $720°$
12. A
13. C
14. D

SECTION 1

Practice and Applications (p. 6-11)

1. **a.** $x < 5$

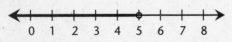

b. $b \geq 7$

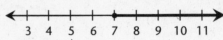

c. $6 < h \leq 14$

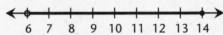

d. $2 < p < 9$

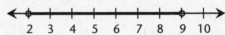

e. $a > 3$

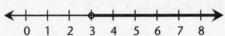

f. $k \leq 6$

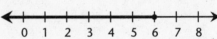

g. $2 < r < 5$

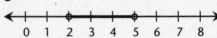

h. $4 < s < 17$

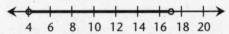

i. $4 < t \leq 16$

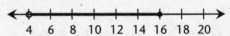

j. $8 < b \leq 10$

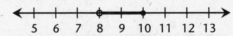

2. **a.** about 5 in. **b.** about 9.5 in.
3. **a.** No; the quadrilateral has only one pair of opposite sides parallel, and a parallelogram has two such pairs. **b.** Yes. **c.** Yes.
4. **a.** concave **b.** convex **c.** concave
5. Sample Response:

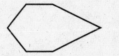

6. **a.** 20 in.^{2} **b.** 22.5 m^2 **c.** 19.76 m^2 **d.** $16\frac{1}{2}$ in.^{2} **e.** 17.55 cm^2
7. **a.** 25 m^2 **b.** 36 cm^2 **c.** 56 ft^2 **d.** 231 cm^2 **e.** 27.5 m^2 **f.** 63 in.^{2}

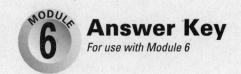

8. a. 84 cm² **b.** 78 in.² **c.** 6 cm **d.** 54 m²
e. 7 cm **f.** 8 ft

9. 225 ft²

Study Guide Exercises (p. 6-15)

1. $w > 5$

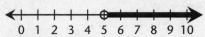

2. $j \le 13$

3. $1 < y < 4$

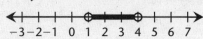

4. $3 < r \le 7$

5. a. wingspans: $9 \text{ ft} \le x \le 10 \text{ ft}$; body lengths: $3.5 \text{ ft} \le x \le 4.6 \text{ ft}$ **b.** No. Sample Response: It is not possible for the body length of one California condor to be greater than the wingspan of another because the two inequalities do not share any of the same values.

6. Yes.

7. No; there is only one pair of parallel sides.

8. concave

9. convex

10. 45 m²

11. 126 ft²

12. 140 cm²

13. 10 m²

14. 3 ft

Quick Quiz (p. 6-16)

1. $15 < x \le 18$

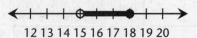

2. $t \ge 175$, where t is the number of minutes Alyssa practices in a given week.

3. Concave; there exists at least two points in the interior of the figure that can be connected by a segment that does not lie entirely in the interior of the polygon.

4. Find the area of the rectangle and the area of the triangle and add the areas together, or use the formula for the area of a trapezoid, $A = \frac{1}{2}(b_1 + b_2)h$.

5. 66 cm²

SECTION 2

Practice and Applications (p. 6-18)

1. a. $\frac{9}{64}$, or about 14% **b.** $\frac{4}{45}$, or about 9%
c. $\frac{9}{16}$, or about 56% **d.** $\frac{2}{3}$, or about 67%
e. $\frac{8}{25}$, or 32% **f.** $\frac{1}{2}$, or 50%

2. a. $\frac{1}{4}$ **b.** 48 m²

3. a. Board B **b.** Board A

4. a. 8.3% **b.** 25% **c.** 25% **d.** 41.7% **e.** 16.7%
f. 33.3%

5.

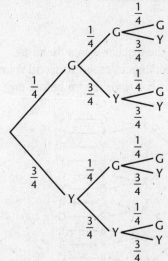

6. a. 1.6% **b.** 42.2% **c.** 4.7% **d.** 14.1%
e. 42.2% **f.** 14.1% **g.** 98.4% **h.** 57.8%

7. a. 62.5% **b.** [tree diagram] **c.** about 14%

d. about 39% **e.** about 23.4%

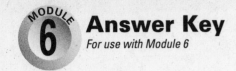
Study Guide Exercises (p. 6-22)

1. $\frac{2}{8} = \frac{1}{4}$, or 25%

2. $\frac{32}{96} = \frac{1}{3}$, or $33\frac{1}{3}$%

3. **a.** 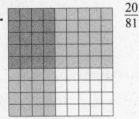 $\frac{20}{81}$

   b.

   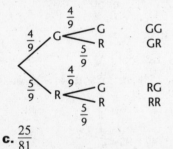

   c. $\frac{25}{81}$

4. **a.** No; since the teacher wants the same number of students in each group, all four cubes would need to be drawn before any were replaced.

   b.

   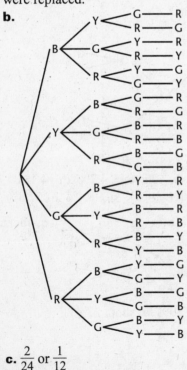

   c. $\frac{2}{24}$ or $\frac{1}{12}$

Quick Quiz (p. 6-23)

1. **a.** $\frac{25}{128}$ or about 19.5% **b.** $\frac{103}{128}$ or about 80.5%

2. $P(\text{2 reds}) = \frac{2}{12} = \frac{1}{6}$

3.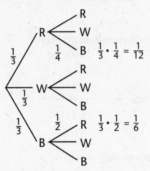

SECTION 3

Practice and Applications (p. 6-26)

1. **a.** $49 = 7 \cdot 7 = 7^2$ **b.** $900 = 30 \cdot 30 = 30^2$
   c. $225 = 15 \cdot 15 = 15^2$

2. **a.** 12 **b.** 6 **c.** 0 **d.** 13 **e.** -4 **f.** -10 **g.** 20
   h. -11 **i.** -9 **j.** -14 **k.** 18 **l.** -16 **m.** 17
   n. -5 **o.** -1 **p.** 8 **q.** 0 **r.** 19

3. **a.** 4 and 5; 4.2 **b.** 6 and 7; 6.8 **c.** 10 and
   11; 10.7 **d.** 5 and 6; 5.5 **e.** 2 and 3; 2.6
   f. 11 and 12; 11.8

4. **a.** 8.5 **b.** 12.6 **c.** 5.3 **d.** 15.2 **e.** 7.5 **f.** 20.4
   g. 8.9 **h.** 6.2 **i.** 15.8 **j.** 7.1 **k.** 11.4 **l.** 16.1
   m. 4.5 **n.** 10.5 **o.** 7.8 **p.** 11.7 **q.** 14.5 **r.** 6.5

5. 28 ft

6. **a.** pentagonal prism **b.** 7 faces, 10 vertices,
   15 edges

7. **a.** octagonal prism **b.** 10 faces, 16 vertices,
   24 edges

8. **a.** Sample Response:

   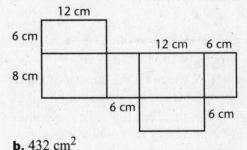

   b. 432 cm^2

Answer Key

For use with Module 6

9. 100 in.^{2}

10, 11. Approximate answers were calculated by using 3.14 for π.

10. **a.** 529π in.^{2}; 1661.06 in.^{2} **b.** 17.64π cm^2; 55.39 cm^2 **c.** 36π m^2; 113.04 m^2 **d.** 225π m^2; 706.50 m^2 **e.** 268.96π cm^2; 844.53 cm^2 **f.** 156.25π ft^2; 490.63 ft^2

11. about 254.34 in.^{2}

Study Guide Exercises (p. 6-30)

1. 11

2. 9

3. −6

4. 12 and 13

5–8. Sample Responses are given.

5. 2.6

6. 6.6

7. 4.5

8. 12.4

9. 0.95 ft

10. a triangular prism

11. 5 faces, 6 vertices, and 9 edges

12. **a.**

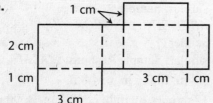

b. 3 cm^2, 3 cm^2, 2 cm^2, 2 cm^2, 6 cm^2, 6 cm^2
c. 22 cm^2

13. 16π mm^2; Sample Responses: 50.24 mm^2 or 50.27 mm^2

14. 7.29π ft^2; Sample Responses: 22.89 ft^2 or 22.90 ft^2

15. 9.61π cm^2; Sample Responses: 30.18 cm^2 or 30.19 cm^2

16. about 5 yd

17. about 3 ft

18. about 6 cm

Quick Quiz (p. 6-31)

1. 20

2. 4 and 5

3. **a.** octagonal prism **b.** 10 faces, 24 edges, and 16 vertices

4. 1120 cm^2

5. 1.44π in.^{2}; 4.52 in.^{2}

Mid-Module Quiz (p. 6-32)

1. $240 \le c \le 275$, where c is the amount in his checking account.

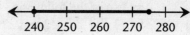

2. **a.** 32 cm^2
b. 28 cm^2
c. $\frac{28}{60}$ or $\frac{7}{15}$

3. **a.**

```
    1 <  1
         2
         3
    2 <  1
         2
         3
```

b. $\frac{1}{6}$
c. $\frac{2}{3}$

4. 10 in.

5. 30

6. 5 and 6

7. trapezoidal prism

8. 6 faces, 12 edges, and 8 vertices

9.

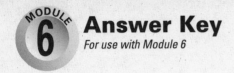
10. 576 in.^{2}

11. 225π mm^2; 706.5 mm^2

12. 3 in.

13. 6.2 cm

SECTION 4

Practice and Applications (p. 6-41)

1. **a.** ∠3, ∠4, ∠5, ∠6 **b.** ∠1, ∠2, ∠7, ∠8
c. ∠3 and ∠5, ∠4 and ∠6 **d.** ∠1 and ∠7, ∠2 and ∠8 **e.** Any two of the following pairs: ∠1 and ∠3, ∠2 and ∠4, ∠5 and ∠7, ∠6 and ∠8 **f.** Any two of the following pairs: ∠1 and ∠5, ∠3 and ∠7, ∠2 and ∠6, ∠4 and ∠8

2. **a.** 127° **b.** 53° **c.** 127° **d.** 53° **e.** 127° **f.** 53°

3. **a.** True. **b.** True. **c.** False. **d.** True. **e.** False. **f.** True. **g.** False. **h.** True. **i.** True. **j.** True. **k.** True. **l.** False.

4. **a.** 47° **b.** 33° **c.** 158° **d.** 118° **e.** 83° **f.** 107° **g.** 121° **h.** 82° **i.** 60°

5. **a.** 100°; obtuse **b.** 84°; acute **c.** 65°; acute **d.** 21°; obtuse **e.** 82°; acute **f.** 90°; right **g.** 128°; obtuse **h.** 94°; obtuse **i.** 79°; right **j.** 78°; acute **k.** 123°; obtuse **l.** 71°; acute

6. 74°

7. **a.** 720° **b.** 1080° **c.** 2340°

Study Guide Exercises (p. 6-45)

1. ∠3, ∠4, ∠5, and ∠6

2. ∠1, ∠2, ∠7, and ∠8

3. ∠3 and ∠6, ∠4 and ∠5

4. ∠1 and ∠4, ∠2 and ∠3, ∠5 and ∠8, ∠6 and ∠7

5. ∠1 and ∠8, ∠2 and ∠7

6. ∠1 and ∠5; ∠2 and ∠6; ∠3 and ∠7; ∠4 and ∠8

7. 128°

8. 52°

9. 128°

10. 128°

11. 52°

12. 52°

13. 90°

14. 50°

15. 60°

16. 43°, 43°

17. 900°

18. 1260°

19. 2160°

20. 179,640°

21. **a.** 24 sides **b.** 165°

Quick Quiz (p. 6-46)

1. ∠1 and ∠3, ∠2 and ∠4, ∠5 and ∠7, or ∠6 and ∠8

2. ∠3 and ∠5, or ∠4 and ∠6

3. ∠1, ∠3, ∠5 and ∠7, or ∠2, ∠4, ∠6 and ∠8

4. 150°

5. **a.** 39° **b.** obtuse

SECTION 5

Practice and Applications (p. 6-49)

1. **a.** congruent; Sample Response: *ABC* ≅ *FED*
b. similar; Sample Response: *ABCDEF* ~ *MNOPQR*
c. neither
d. similar; Sample Response: *JKLM* ~ *ABCD*

2. **a.** 5.4 m **b.** 0.6 m **c.** 4.8 m

3. **a.** 12 mm **b.** 30 mm **c.** 60 mm **d.** 90 mm **e.** 108 mm **f.** 120 mm

4. 210 mi

5. **a.** $\overline{PQ}$, $\overline{QR}$ **b.** 104°, 29°, 47° **c.** 4.5 cm, 6.75 cm

6. **a.** ∠*ZWX*, 90° **b.** 126°, 65.5°, 78.5° **c.** *CD*, 20 ft **d.** 36 ft, 48 ft

7. **a.** ∠*LIJ*, 60° **b.** 120°, 90°, 90° **c.** $\overline{JK}$, 8 m **d.** 10 m, 11 m

8. 9 cm

9. No. For triangles to be similar, their angle measures must be equivalent and the lengths of their sides proportional. Although all right triangles have one angle that measures 90°,

Answer Key

For use with Module 6

the measures of the other two angles of right triangles are not necessarily equivalent. For example, 90°–45°–45° and 90°–60°–30° are both possible measures of the angles in a right triangle.

Study Guide Exercises (p. 6-53)

1. 30 mm
2. 200 mm
3. 400 mm
4. similar; $ABC \sim DEF$
5. neither
6. neither
7. congruent; $OPQRST \cong VWXYZU$
8. 0.6 m
9. 0.3 m
10. 0.2 m
11. $\overline{FG}$; $\overline{GH}$; $\overline{EH}$
12. 110°; 110°; 70°; 70°
13. $1\frac{1}{2}$ in.; 3 in.; $1\frac{1}{2}$ in.
14. Sample Response:

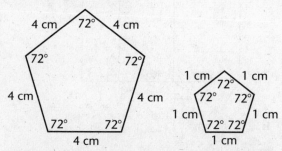

The corresponding angles of the two pentagons have the same measures, and the corresponding sides are proportional.

Quick Quiz (p. 6-54)

1. Check students' work.
2. $ABCDE \sim ZVWXY$
3. 19 in.
4. **a.** $\angle EHG$; 40° **b.** 4 ft; 2.5 ft

END-OF-MODULE RESOURCES AND ASSESSMENTS

Practice and Applications, Sections 1–5 (p. 6-55)

1. **a.** convex **b.** concave **c.** convex
2. **a.** 44 in.^{2} **b.** 84 cm^2
3. **a.** 14 m **b.** 105 mm^2 **c.** 13 ft
4. 64%
5. **a.** 14 and 15 **b.** –15 **c.** 11 **d.** –3 and –4
6. Approximate answers were calculated by using 3.14 for π. **a.** 30.25π in.^{2}; 94.99 in.^{2} **b.** 68.89π cm^2; 216.31 cm^2 **c.** 441π m^2; 1384.74 m^2
7. **a.** 42° **b.** 42° **c.** 138° **d.** 138° **e.** 42° **f.** 138°
8. **a.** similar; $CDAB \sim WXYZ$ or $WZYX \sim CDAB$ **b.** neither
9. 300 mi
10. 15 mm or 1.5 cm
11. **a.** 71°, 83°, 60° **b.** 11 ft, 18 ft, 12 ft

Test Form A (p. 6-58)

1. $200 \leq p \leq 360$, where p is the number of passengers on the cruise.

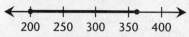

2. $m \geq 40$, where m is the number of minutes Sara practices each day.

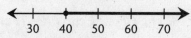

3. Sample Response:

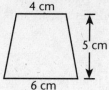

4. **a.** $\frac{5}{16}$

   b. $\frac{11}{16}$

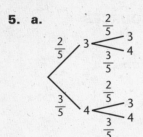
5. a.

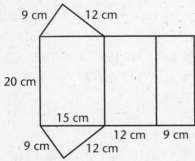

b. P(sum of 7) $= \dfrac{12}{25}$

6. 13 and 14

7. 22

8. a.

9 cm   12 cm

20 cm

15 cm

9 cm   12 cm

12 cm   9 cm

b. 828 cm^2

9. 900π mm^2; 2826 mm^2

10. 16π in.^{2}; 50.2 in.^{2}

11. $m\angle 1 = 100°$; $m\angle 2 = 80°$; $m\angle 3 = 100°$;
$m\angle 4 = 100°$; $m\angle 5 = 80°$; $m\angle 6 = 100°$;
$m\angle 7 = 80°$

12. a. 90° **b.** right triangle

13. 1800°

14. a. $BC = 18\frac{2}{3}$ cm; $CD = 5\frac{1}{3}$ cm; $PN = 7\frac{1}{2}$ cm

b. The corresponding angles of the two polygons are congruent. That is, $m\angle A = m\angle P$, $m\angle B = m\angle L$, $m\angle C = m\angle M$, and $m\angle D = m\angle N$.

Test Form B (p. 6-60)

1. $0 \le l \le 3000$, where l is the permissible load for the elevator.

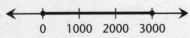

0   1000   2000   3000

2. $f \ge 500$, where f is the number of pounds of food eaten by an elephant per day.

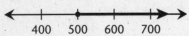

400   500   600   700

3.

7 cm

5 cm

9 cm

4. a. $\frac{1}{5}$ **b.** $\frac{4}{5}$

5. a.

$\frac{4}{5}$ 3 $\frac{4}{5}$ 3
              $\frac{1}{5}$ 5

$\frac{1}{5}$ 5 $\frac{4}{5}$ 3
              $\frac{1}{5}$ 5

b. P(sum is 8) $= \dfrac{8}{25}$

6. 7 and 8

7. 26

8. a.

4 cm   6 cm

12.8 cm

7.2 cm   6 cm   4 cm

4 cm   6 cm

b. 244.16 cm^2

9. 25π ft^2; 78.5 ft^2

10. 331.24π cm^2; 1040.1 cm^2

11. $m\angle 1 = 140°$; $m\angle 2 = 40°$; $m\angle 3 = 140°$;
$m\angle 4 = 140°$; $m\angle 5 = 40°$; $m\angle 6 = 140°$;
$m\angle 7 = 40°$

12. a. 110° **b.** obtuse triangle

13. 1440°

14. a. $WX = 7.2$ cm; $BC = 20$ cm; $YW = 12$ cm

b. The corresponding angles of the two polygons are congruent. That is,
$m\angle A = m\angle X$, $m\angle B = m\angle Z$, $m\angle C = m\angle Y$,
and $m\angle D = m\angle W$.

Answer Key

For use with Module 6

Standardized Test (p. 6-62)

1. b
2. b
3. b
4. c
5. a
6. c
7. a
8. b
9. d
10. c

Performance Assessment (p. 6-63)

1. **Anastasia's Plan** $S.A. = 3800 \text{ ft}^2$
   $V = 12{,}000 \text{ ft}^3$
   $\frac{S.A.}{V} \approx 0.32$

   Beulah's Plan $S.A. = 3800 \text{ ft}^2$
   $V = 12{,}000 \text{ ft}^3$
   $\frac{S.A.}{V} \approx 0.32$

   Chrysilla's Plan $S.A. \approx 3680 \text{ ft}^2$
   $V = 12{,}000 \text{ ft}^3$
   $\frac{S.A.}{V} \approx 0.31$

2. They should use Chrysilla's house because it has the lowest surface-area-to-volume ratio.

3. **Anastasia's New Plan** $S.A. = 8550 \text{ ft}^2$
   $V = 40{,}500 \text{ ft}^3$
   $\frac{S.A.}{V} \approx 0.21$

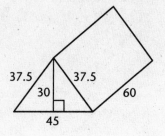

Beulah's New Plan $S.A. = 8550 \text{ ft}^2$
$V = 40{,}500 \text{ ft}^3$
$\frac{S.A.}{V} \approx 0.21$

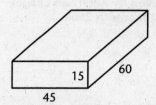

Chrysilla's New Plan $S.A. \approx 8286 \text{ ft}^2$
$V = 40{,}500 \text{ ft}^3$
$\frac{S.A.}{V} \approx 0.20$

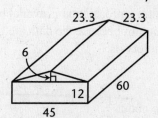

4. Beulah is correct. The ratios change as the dimensions increase.

Answer Key
For use after Modules 5 and 6

Modules 5 and 6 Cumulative Test (p. CT-1)

1. $3.60/lb

2. 4.7°/hr

3. **Games Won by American League Baseball Teams in 2006**

```
6 | 1 2
7 | 0 8 8
8 | 0 6 7 9
9 | 0 3 5 6 7
```

   6 | 1 represents 61 games

4. range = 36, mean = 83, median = 86.5, mode = 78

5. 7

6. None of this information is available from the histogram because the data are given only in intervals.

7. 9.45

8. 275

9. **a.** 36 **b.** about $\frac{1}{4}$

10. 58.1%

11. 50

12. 288

13. Sample Response: I expect to have to work from the time I am 21 years old until I am 65; $21 \le x \le 65$.

14. $\frac{7}{30}$

15. **a.**

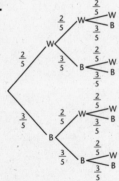

   b. $\frac{12}{125}$, 0.096, 9.6%

16. between 10 and 11

17. 30

18. **a.**

```
      12 in.
5 in. ╱────
6 in. │ 13 cm │      │    │
5 in. ╲────
      12 in.   12 in.  5 in.
```

   b. 240 in.^{2}

19. 7.29π in.^{2}; about 22.9 in.^{2}

20. **a.** 51° **b.** obtuse

21. $JL = 25$ cm, $BC = 96$ cm

22. $m\angle 1 = m\angle 2 = m\angle 7 = m\angle 5 = 82°$, $m\angle 3 = m\angle 4 = m\angle 6 = 98°$